LIVING IN THE

REAL

BIBLICAL REALITIES FOR LIFE

REGULAR BAPTIST PRESS

The Doctrinal Basis of Our Curriculum

A more detailed statement with references is available upon request.

- The verbal, plenary inspiration of the Scriptures
- Only one true God
- The Trinity of the Godhead
- The Holy Spirit and His ministry
- The personality of Satan
- The Genesis account of creation
- Original sin and the fall of man
- The virgin birth of Christ
- Salvation through faith in the shed blood of Christ
- The bodily resurrection and priesthood of Christ
- Grace and the new birth
- Justification by faith
- Sanctification of the believer
- The security of the believer
- The church
- The ordinances of the local church: baptism by immersion and the Lord's Supper
- Biblical separation— ecclesiastical and personal
- Obedience to civil government
- The place of Israel
- The pretribulation rapture of the church
- The premillennial return of Christ
- The millennial reign of Christ
- Eternal glory in Heaven for the righteous
- Eternal torment in Hell for the wicked

Alex Bauman, Writer and Editor

Living in the Real: Biblical Realities for Life
Adult Bible Study Student Book
Vol. 63 • No. 1
© 2014 • Regular Baptist Press
www.regularbaptistpress.org • 1-800-727-4440
Printed in U.S.A.
All rights reserved
RBP0114 • ISBN: 978-1-60776-930-9

Contents

Preface

What is real?

That question is harder for people to answer now than perhaps ever before. The line between real and fiction is blurred in many people's minds. They are so used to living a lie that it has become their reality.

Perhaps you have adopted this approach to life and have turned your spiritual life into a display. Maybe your persona is more important than your heart, and your reputation is more important than your relationships with God.

The apostle Paul sounded alarms to three churches that had lost touch with reality. He told them to WAKE UP! It could be that you need to hear those same alarms. Those alarms form the starting point for this course.

Living in the Real will encourage you to honestly examine your life in light of God's Word. It will confront you with the need to live according to Biblical realities. It will emphasize how the truth about God, the Bible, Christ, the Holy Spirit, the church, and future reward and judgment should shape and direct your life.

Believers who live in the real will produce real fruit. Their lives will be useful to God and will bear everlasting results.

Believers who ignore Biblical realities are living a lie and wasting their lives. Their fruit, like the digital apple on the cover, is just for show; it has no real value as fruit.

This course will confront you with Biblical realities and challenge you to examine your life in light of those realities. And it will encourage you to approach future study of God's Word with honesty and with a desire to grow.

Pray for yourself as you complete this study. Ask God to wake you from any pretentious living and to drive you to live in the real that your life might be characterized by real fruit with everlasting results.

Wake Up!

Exod 3.13-14
Acts 17,28
Heb 11.6

▶ Scripture Focus

Rom. 13:11–14; 1 Cor. 15:30–34; Eph. 5:3–17

Theme

God wants us to live by Biblical realities and have a real impact on the world.

Memory Verses

"Wherefore he saith, Awake thou that sleepest, and arise from the dead, and Christ shall give thee light. See then that ye walk circumspectly, not as fools, but as wise, redeeming the time, because the days are evil" (Ephesians 5:14–16).

GETTING STARTED

Sleepwalking can be quite scary. Some people even sleep drive. A young woman used to get up in the middle of the night, drive down the highway to her brother's house, honk the car horn, and then drive back home. To keep her from doing it again, her friends tied her to her bed each night.

1. Tell about a time when you walked or talked in your sleep.

2. How might you describe "spiritual sleepwalking"?

Even as believers we have a tendency to spiritually sleepwalk through life. Without realizing it, we become out of touch with reality. God wants us to live in the real and have a real impact on the world, so He has given us Biblical realities for life. This course will challenge you to live in light of those Biblical realities.

Our Flesh Demands Control

God is real, and He wants us as believers to live in reality (Heb. 11:6). That sounds agreeable. But living in reality is not something you just decide to do. It is a lifelong battle made up of daily decisions to follow God in the power of the Spirit (Rom. 6:11–14; 7:22, 23).

As sinners, people believe the lies that there is no higher person than self and no higher purposes than personal satisfaction, pleasure, and recognition. Even as believers, our flesh, or sin nature, believes these lies. Our flesh desperately wants us to live according to them. It is committed to the lies, never wavering in its dedication and devotion.

3. Read Isaiah 53:6. What clear message does this verse give about our flesh, our sin nature?

4. Read Proverbs 12:15. Why is the person who thinks his way is right called a fool?

The word "reality" could be substituted for the word "way" in both Isaiah 53:6 and Proverbs 12:15. Everyone creates his own reality, believes it is true, and turns from God, the ultimate reality. Without God's intervention on our behalf, we would all be forever lost.

Our Flesh Creates False Realities

After placing our trust in Christ for salvation, we as believers should know better than to create our own reality, but we do it anyway. Our reasons for creating false realities fall into five categories.

Some of us want to create a world in which we are at the controls. We want to call the shots in our lives and determine what is right and wrong. Our reality makes it okay for us to write all the "rules" to our own liking.

Others of us want to create a reality that excuses us from the responsibilities of being a believer. We see living the Christian life as a burden and perhaps even a bore. When we consider living for Christ, we see a list of restrictions and demands instead of a Person. We are too busy, not talented enough, or too overwhelmed with life to contribute to the cause of Christ.

Some of us create a world in which spirituality is just for show. We seek recognition for being spiritual under false pretenses. We want people to praise us for what they think we are.

Relieving guilt is another reason for creating our own reality. We enjoy sin and don't like to feel guilty or convicted when we sin. So we make up our own world in which our sin is okay.

And some of us think we simply don't matter to God and that He doesn't care what we do in our little corners of the world. We imagine a God Who is too big to bother with us. So we do our own thing in life as if it doesn't matter in the end.

5. What other reasons might a believer have for creating a reality?

6. Which of the reasons for creating one's own reality have you seen in your life?

7. Which ones might you recognize in your life right now?

Live in the Real—Awake to Righteousness

God directed Paul to write to three churches about living in the real. Some in the church at Corinth had created a reality that made it okay for them to commit indulgent sins. Paul gave the church a wake-up call.

Paul put his life on the line daily for the sake of the gospel and the the resurrection in particular (1 Cor. 15:30, 31). Paul even "fought with beasts at Ephesus" (15:32), perhaps a reference to literal wild animals. He willingly lived in jeopardy because God is real and worth living and dying for.

Paul's life of jeopardy stood in stark contrast to the Corinthians' indulgent lives. The indulgent Corinthians rejected a future resurrection of believers in order to excuse their sin. They created their own reality in which what they did with their bodies did not matter since God was not going to resurrect their bodies. They believed they should live for pleasure now, for perhaps "tomorrow" they would die (15:32).

8. Read 1 Corinthians 15:3–8. How established is the reality of Christ's resurrection?

9. Read 1 Corinthians 15:20–23. What is the important connection between Christ's resurrection and the resurrection of believers?

The indulgent Corinthians were bold in creating a reality that denied the resurrection in that it struck at the core of the gospel. Obviously Paul took their actions seriously and called on the rest of the church at Corinth to respond.

Those who denied the resurrection were corrupt and in a sense "contagious." Believers who embraced the true doctrine of the resurrection needed to separate themselves from those who denied the resurrection (15:33).

Paul told the Corinthians to wake up to righteousness and resist living in a dream world (15:34). They could not just make up reality because reality is based in God's person. All attempts at reality outside of God are dreams and lies. To create a new reality would be to change God. That cannot happen.

10. Read Malachi 3:6, Psalm 102:24–27, and James 1:17. What do these passages teach about the changeableness of God?

Paul went on to point out that the Corinthians needed to resist living in a dream world because some did not have a knowledge of God (1 Cor. 15:34). The Corinthian believers were God's vessels for shining the light of the gospel before the lost. If they as God's vessels were filthy, then the gospel's light would be dim and rendered ineffective. They needed to live righteously before the wicked.

11. Read 1 Corinthians 15:34. How should the Corinthians have responded to Paul's condemnation of living in a dream world?

The "dreaming" Corinthians were enjoying fleeting moments of pleasure instead of sharing eternal life with those facing eternity in the torments of the Lake of Fire.

Imagine the Corinthians watching unbelievers plunged into the Lake of Fire as they call after them, "I'm so sorry you are about to experience agonizing, eternal torment. I was too busy living in my own dream world to tell you about the reality of eternity without God." Such a scene would never happen, but it is what Paul wanted the Corinthians to consider.

12. How should you respond when you understand the connection between reality and eternity?

Live in the Real—Put on the Armor of Light

Paul gave the Romans a similar message about living in a dream world.

13. Read Romans 13:11. Why is "sleep" a good analogy for living out of touch with reality?

Paul called on the Romans to awake out of sleep as the reality of Christ's return drew near (Rom. 13:11, 12). The "night" refers to the present time when Christ is not on the earth and Satan is working. The "day" that is at hand is the return of Christ. In a sense, the return of Christ is always at hand because Christ's promised return is at any moment (Rev. 22:7, 12). We are to be living with urgency because our time to serve God and reach others for Christ in this age is limited.

Paul again used the day and night contrast as he described how the Romans should live in light of Christ's return (Rom. 13:13). Paul told them to cast off the works of darkness and to put on the armor of light instead (13:12; cf. Eph. 6:10–18).

14. Read Romans 13:12, 14 and Ephesians 6:10–18. Why would putting on the armor of light be the same as putting on the Lord Jesus Christ? Consider how each piece of armor describes Christ.

Putting on the armor of light and putting on Christ are both akin to living in the real. Our lives should be characterized by Christlikeness. That happens only when we live in God's reality rather than in the dream world our flesh created. That is why Paul told the Romans not to make any provisions for the flesh to fulfill its lusts (Rom. 13:14). To make "provision" means to "plan out ways" to indulge the flesh.

15. What might stimulate a person to make provisions for the flesh?

The armor of light protects us from living according to the lies our flesh and the devil want us to adopt (Eph. 6:11–13). Appropriately, "truth" is associated with the belt, the first piece of the armor we are to put on. We put on the belt of truth by immersing ourselves in God's Word, the source of truth. Attached to our belt of truth is the sword of the Spirit, which is the Word of God (6:17). So our protection from living in a dream world begins with truth. And that truth, as found in the Word of God, becomes our offensive weapon to defeat the devil and his lies. Putting on the armor of light, beginning with the belt of truth, is crucial to living in the real.

Live in the Real—Walk in the Light

Paul's instructions to the Corinthians and Romans are echoed in his letter to the Ephesians. Paul encouraged the Ephesians to walk as children of light (Eph. 5:8b). "Goodness and righteousness and truth" characterize those who walk as "children of light" (5:9). Conversely, God's wrath comes on those who walk as "sons of disobedience" (5:3–6). Paul wanted the Ephesians to find that fact motivating. If they did not shine the light of God's love to the lost, then how would the lost escape the darkness and God's coming wrath?

Paul pointed to the role of the Spirit in making it possible for a believer to walk in the light (5:9). "Goodness and righteousness and truth" is the "fruit" that comes from living by the Spirit. "Goodness" is showing love to others. "Righteousness" refers to our character from God's perspective. "Truth" is essentially reality. We live according to God's Word, the source of truth, when we live by the Spirit.

The more we walk in the light, the more in touch we become with reality. We learn what is acceptable to the Lord (5:10), and it shows in our lives.

As we walk in the light, our lives will contrast the "darkness" around us. Paul told the Ephesians to "reprove" the "unfruitful works of darkness" (5:11). As we walk in the light and live in reality, we will expose people's lives. The realities they have created for themselves will be shown to be lies.

16. What are some of the lies the lost order their lives by?

17. Read Ephesians 5:12, 13. How might a believer expose "unfruitful works of darkness"?

God doesn't want us walking in the light instead of "sleeping" (5:14). Paul told the "drowsy" Ephesians to "awake." They needed a dose of reality. "Look around you, Ephesian believers!" Paul essentially told them. "The world desperately needs to see the light of the truth! Stop living in darkness like the lost so they will see the truth and respond."

The word "circumspectly" in verse 15 means to look around. We must take time to look around us and consider reality. Doing so is wise. Wisdom is seeing life from God's perspective and responding accordingly. Ignoring reality is foolish.

Our time to walk in the light and introduce the lost to the reality of Christ is limited. Paul instructed the Ephesians to redeem, or buy up, their time (5:16). "Time" refers to a critical period of time or a special opportunity. Every believer's life is critical to the cause of Christ. Your life is critical to the cause of Christ! That is reality!

Instead of seeking to make sense of life, finding our way, or trying to build a legacy, we should be focused on understanding God's will (5:17). That means living in reality. The Bible contains all the Biblical realities for life we need to know. This course will help you recognize those Biblical realities so you might live wide awake and might walk in the light as Christ intends.

MAKING IT PERSONAL

18. Have you been living in a dream world or in reality? What would you cite as evidence for your conclusion?

19. What advantages might you hope to gain by living in a dream world?

20. Do you fear living by Biblical realities? What are those fears?

Answering questions like these takes more than a few moments. Sometimes we have so carefully constructed our lives that we fail to see we are living in disobedience to God. And our flesh is going to fight to convince us that we are fine. A true evaluation of ourselves should be ongoing and guided by Scripture and the Spirit. This study will help you with that process.

21. What could you do to begin to live according to Biblical realities? Add to the following ideas.

- Be honest with God about your life.
- Take sin in your life seriously.
- Block out extended periods of time for prayer and renewal of your relationship with God.
- Put on the belt of truth by studying God's Word daily.
- Strap on the sword of the Spirit by memorizing Bible verses that speak directly to your tendency to live in a pretend world.
- Study the Biblical realities in this course faithfully and thoughtfully.
- Seek godly counseling from your pastor or a trusted fellow believer.
- Find an accountability partner to specifically monitor whether you are living in the real.

22. What *will* you do to begin to live according to Biblical realities?

God Is

▶ **Scripture Focus**

Exod. 3; 14; 15; Acts 17:28; Heb. 11:1, 6

Theme

God is the ultimate reality.

> **Memory Verse**
> *"But without faith it is impossible to please him:*
> *for he that cometh to God must believe that he is,*
> *and that he is a rewarder of them that diligently seek him"*
> *(Hebrews 11:6).*

GETTING STARTED

Social media has helped people create unrealistic personas. They embellish their accomplishments, hide their weaknesses, and lie about their failures. Their "social media me" is a far better person than their real me.

1. How much do you trust what people post about themselves on social media sites?

2. Do you think you have ever been fooled by someone's "social media me"? Explain.

People are easy to fool. But God cannot be fooled. We could say the "God me" is the person we really are—the person God sees and knows perfectly. God wants to change our "God me" into the image of His Son. Understanding the Biblical reality of God is a crucial step in that process.

God Is the Ultimate Reality

God gives us Biblical realities for life so that we might live in the real. The Biblical reality of God is where we must begin.

3.   Read Hebrews 11:1, 6. How would you describe "faith"?

The writer of Hebrews provides a description of faith. Faith is trusting that God is real. A person of faith orders his life according to the belief that everything about God is true, including all His promises and attributes. The "things hoped for" in Hebrews 11:1 are the future rewards God promises the believer. The "things not seen" (11:1) are God's attributes. God's self-existence, eternality, holiness, omnipotence, sovereignty, omniscience, and omnipresence are all included in the "things not seen." This lesson focuses on those attributes so we might better understand Who God is.

It takes genuine faith to please God (11:6), so no one could please God by making up his own definition of Who God is. And no one could create his own "rules" for what pleases God. He must believe that God "is" without adding or subtracting from what God reveals about Himself in His Word.

God rewards those who "diligently seek him" in His Word and discover what He is like and what He expects of them (11:6). Lazy study of God's Word leads to bad theology, a weak faith, and a shallow spiritual life. We can't expect to grow in our understanding of and relationship with God by plopping open our Bibles and reading until we find something that inspires us or makes us feel better. We must commit to knowing God as He is and resist the temptation to define God to our liking.

God Is Self-defining

Our culture prizes personal views and opinions, so people accept and even celebrate personal definitions of God. The only view of God they don't accept is the view that claims exclusivity. Society doesn't like a view of God that excludes all other views. Of course, the Bible presents an exclusive view of God because the Bible presents truth.

4. When has someone rejected you because your belief in God does not allow for contrary opinions?

While specific personal opinions about God are too many to list, most opinions about God fall into three categories. The first category is that **God is a distant, impersonal being**. Those who hold this view believe that God doesn't communicate or interact with people. He is uninterested in what people do. He doesn't care if they are good or bad. Proponents of this view see themselves as *free from* God.

In the second category is the belief that **God is an ogre** waiting to punish people for doing wrong. Those who adopt this view of God believe people should live in fear that at any moment God will bring trouble into their lives. From this perspective, living with God is like living with an easily angered grump. Those who hold this opinion of God are characterized by *fear of* God.

In the third category is the belief that **God is a celestial Santa Claus**. Those who hold this view believe God will grant them favors and protect them from bad circumstances as long as they are good. Those who hold this opinion of God are characterized by seeking *favor from* God.

Overall, a growing number in society hold that Who God is to one person can be different than Who God is to another person. But both are right even if the two people call God by different names and describe Him as two completely different Persons. In reality, God is self-defining. He speaks to His identity in His inspired Word.

The truth about God is central to living in reality. The apostle Paul addressed a group of Athenian pagans on Mars' Hill while he was on one of his missionary journeys. Paul introduced them to God as the One in Whom "we live, and move, and have our being" (Acts 17:28). We exist because God is real. We could not live without Him. And we certainly don't have the right to define God based on a personal view or opinion. *Faith in* God should characterize our relationship with God, rather than freedom from God, terrifying fear of God, or seeking favors from God.

God's revelations of Himself to the Israelites as they left Egypt and established themselves as a nation in the wilderness provide us with informative settings for learning about God. The Israelites knew little about God even though they were called to be His people. So God used crises and triumphs to reveal Himself to them.

The Red Sea crossing was one of the most furtive learning experiences for Israel (Exod. 14). Consequently, it became an important event in Israel's history. Decades after the Red Sea crossing, the people of Jericho talked about Israel's God in fear as Israel prepared to conquer the Promised Land (Josh. 2:8–10). When Israel did enter the Promised Land, Joshua put memorial stones up in the Jordan and in Gilgal to remind generations to come about the crossing (Josh. 4:21–24). And Ezra and Nehemiah spoke about the Red Sea crossing nearly a thousand years later as they led a remnant of Jews in a spiritual renewal (Neh. 9:9–12). God intended for the Red Sea crossing to reveal truths about Himself that Israel would remember for generations.

God Is Self-existent and Eternal

God called Moses to be His leader in preparation for the Exodus and Red Sea crossing (Exod. 3:13, 14). In response, Moses wanted to know what God is like. He asked God about His "name" (3:13). God's "name" represents Who God is. God answered by telling Moses that He is "I AM WHO I AM" (3:14). In other words, God is self-existent; He needs no one. God is complete without anyone else. He is neither lonely nor deficient on His own.

5.   What are some implications of God's self-existence?

God's self-existence was important for Moses and for Israel especially as they labored under the heavy hand of Pharaoh, the leader of Egypt. Egypt was a military juggernaut with horses and strong chariots. Escaping would have been impossible for the Israelites. But with the I AM on their side, deliverance was guaranteed (3:16, 17).

God continued revealing Himself to Moses. He emphasized His eternality, an attribute tied to God's self-existence (3:15). Moses needed to know that the God Who called Abraham to the Promised Land was still around and would be for all generations. But God also wanted Moses to know that He has always been around and always would be. God is eternal. There has never been a time when God was not the I AM, and there could never be a time when God would cease to be the I AM.

6. Why is thinking of God's self-existence and eternality so troubling for our minds?

7. How should the reality of God's self-existence and eternality impact a believer's life?

Rev. 4.8
God Is Holy

Other aspects of God's self-revelation are captured in the song Moses wrote after crossing the Red Sea. Pharaoh's horses, chariots, and riders were drowned as they attempted to chase after the Children of Israel (15:1–5). Some of the dead Egyptians washed up on the shore of the Red Sea as evidence of God's great deliverance. Israel was free at last. This caused a Moses-led celebration of God. Moses focused on God's holiness by including two rhetorical questions in his song.

8. Read Exodus 15:11. What point do these rhetorical questions make?

God is truly unique. No one could even imagine a god comparable to the one true God. None could ever be like Him. God is "glorious," or majestic, in His holiness. Holiness refers to God's perfect nature; He is absolutely free from sin. His perfection is so majestic and bright that no one could look on Him and live (33:20).

Isaiah and John both saw heavenly scenes where the holiness of God was a central focus (Isa. 6:1–3; Rev. 4:8). The continuous repetition of "holy, holy, holy" at those scenes speaks to the perfection of God's holiness as well as the wonder of it. God's holiness is so compelling that the angels can't stop talking about it.

God's holiness was later given to Israel as the standard for their lives (Lev. 11:44, 45). They were to be holy because God is holy. Peter repeated this command for believers today.

9. Read 1 Peter 1:13–16. What parts of your life should emulate the holiness of God?

10. How should God's holiness affect your perspective on the seriousness of sin, particularly any sins you don't consider offensive?

Being holy, or separated from sin unto God, is an ongoing, daily goal for us as believers. It requires effort and reliance on God to renew our minds through His Word (Eph. 4:17–24). Though we will not be completely free from sin in this life, we know that one day we will be. When Christ returns for His church, we will receive glorified bodies and be forever free from our sin nature (Phil. 3:20, 21).

11. How should the holiness of God impact a believer's life?

Exod 26

God Is Omnipotent and Sovereign

God showed His omnipotence and sovereignty earlier in the Red Sea crossing account. "Omnipotence" means "all-powerful," while "sovereignty" refers to God's absolute control. God led the Children of Israel from Egypt to Pi Hahiroth, an inescapable place next to the Red Sea. He told Moses that He wanted them to camp there on purpose so He could use their position to lure Pharaoh from Egypt and destroy his army. Moses even told the people that God was leading them to Pi Hahiroth for the purpose of destroying Pharaoh's army (Exod. 14:1–4). God hardened

Pharaoh's heart as part of His plan. The Egyptian king, unaware of God's sovereign plan, came out with his best forces to capture Israel (14:8).

Once the Israelites saw the horses and chariots pursuing them, they became very nervous. They had nowhere to turn but to God. They cried out to Him (14:10), but their subsequent complaints to Moses revealed their lack of faith (14:11, 12). In reality, they did not trust God to keep His word. They did not believe He was sovereignly in control of Pharaoh and his army. They soon learned otherwise as God protected them, powerfully parted the Red Sea, and then destroyed the Egyptian army.

In the aftermath of the destruction of the Egyptian army, Moses focused on God's omnipotence and sovereignty in his song to God.

12. Read Exodus 15:2. How might thinking about God's omnipotence and sovereignty affect your life right now?

The salvation God gave Moses through His power and leading caused Moses to rejoice and sing. Moses recognized that God had sovereignly led them and then delivered them by His strength. He was amazed by God. Moses went on to sing that God's right hand became "glorious in power" (15:6). The word "glorious" has the idea of "wide" or "broad." Moses was pointing out how illustrious God's power is. It amazed him.

We know God's power is real, but when we personally benefit from it, our understanding of it grows. It becomes awesome. We should live every day with a deep appreciation of God's omnipotence and sovereignty.

13. What in your life has caused you to have a broader understanding of God's power and sovereignty?

14. How should the omnipotence and sovereignty of God impact a believer's life?

God Is Omniscient and Omnipresent

Backing up in the account once more, we again see God showing His attributes. As Israel encamped by the Red Sea with the Egyptian army closing in, God's presence with them was obvious. God was in a cloud that darkened the night for the Egyptians and provided comfort and light for the Israelites (14:19, 20). Israel actually witnessed the cloud move from before them to behind them to protect them from the Egyptian army. It was as if God was saying, "Don't worry. I'm here. I know the danger you are in. I will protect you with My presence."

15. Read Philippians 4:6, 7. How do the truths that God is all-knowing (omniscient) and everywhere-present at all times (omnipresent) help you understand this passage?

The Israelites needed to understand their God is omniscient and omnipresent as they made their way to the Promised Land. Moses anticipated God's presence with Israel and sang about God leading and guiding them to His "holy habitation" (15:13). Moses was confident God's presence would "bring" the Israelites into the Promised Land (15:17).

16. How should the omniscience and omnipresence of God impact a believer's life?

After celebrating God, the Israelites camped at Mount Sinai. There they dishearteningly revealed their desire to define God for themselves despite God's miraculous revelation of Himself at the Red Sea. While Moses was on the mountain conversing with God, God's people had Aaron create a golden calf to represent the god who brought them out of Egypt (Exod. 32:1–4). By creating the calf, the Israelites claimed the right to determine what their god expected of them and found acceptable. Sensuality and drunkenness were at the top of their list of acceptable practices. They partied as they danced around their god (32:19). Ironically, the one true God was in the middle of giving Moses the Ten Commandments, the beginning of the law that would define for Israel what God expected of them as His covenant people.

We, like the Israelites, have a sin nature that wants to control and define God. Instead, we must put our faith in Him and believe that He "is" (Heb. 11:6).

MAKING IT PERSONAL

17. What does your life reveal about what you actually believe about God? Prayerfully consider this answer.

18. Review questions 7, 11, 14, and 16. Which of the responses to God's person are true of your life? Which ones are not true of your life?

19. What would be some consequences of continuing to have wrong beliefs about God?

20. What steps will you take to adjust your beliefs about God?

God Relates

▶ Scripture Focus

Gen. 3; 12:1–3; Neh. 9; Jer. 31:3; Lam. 3:22, 23; John 3:16;
Rom. 3:21–26; 5:17–21; 8:38, 39; 1 John 1:9

Theme

God is a person Who relates to humanity according to His holiness.

Memory Verse

"Thou, even thou, art Lord alone; thou hast made heaven, the heaven of heavens, with all their host, the earth, and all things that are therein, the seas, and all that is therein, and thou preservest them all; and the host of heaven worshippeth thee"
(Nehemiah 9:6).

GETTING STARTED

You come home to find your cat tore up your brand new curtains. Your teenager hands you his $300 speeding ticket. Your boss gives you coveted tickets to an upcoming sporting event. Your daughter does the dishes of her own volition. Your boys eat everything in the frig. Everything!

1. On what basis would you respond to the people in the scenarios?

2. On what basis does God relate to people?

The last study presented God's holiness. This study will help you understand how God's holiness affects His relationships with humanity.

The previous study left off with Israel's desire to define Who God is. They showed that desire at Mount Sinai (Exod. 32) and later when they were in the Promised Land (1 Kings 16:29–34).

Eventually God judged His people for their rebellion against Him. He used Assyria in 722 BC to take the Northern Kingdom of Israel captive, and He used Babylon in 586 BC to take the Southern Kingdom of Judah captive. Israel never returned from captivity, while a small remnant of Jews from the Southern Kingdom returned to the Promised Land about 50 years after Jerusalem fell.

The remnant rebuilt the temple and repaired the walls, which were in ruins. When the walls were finished, Ezra read from the book of the law and explained it to the people (Neh. 8:1, 2). As the people reflected on their history and their continuing captivity in the Promised Land, they understood how unfaithful they had been as a nation. In response, they confessed their sins and worshiped God (9:3).

As part of Israel's worship and confession, the Levites led in a public prayer. They stood on an ascent and prayed with a loud voice to God for all the people to hear (9:4, 5). Their theme was God's faithfulness to their unfaithful nation. They recounted how God had treated them and related to them as a nation. God is the main character in their prayer. What they said about God helps us understand that He is relational and that He always acts based on His perfect, holy character.

The Levites' informative prayer will be the basis for this lesson on God's person and relationship to humanity.

God Is a Personal Creator

The Levites began their prayer with an acknowledgement of how great God's name is (9:5). They called on the people to stand and bless the Lord. The Levites then turned their attention to God and addressed Him directly.

3. Read Nehemiah 9:6. Why is the statement that God alone is the Lord so important?

If Israel learned anything over their history, it was that God alone is the Lord. Formal idolatry actually ceased to be a problem in Israel after their return from captivity, though that didn't mean they lived like they should. They had other problems such as insincere ritualism in their worship, mistreatment of others, and immorality.

4. What responsibilities to God come with being part of His creation (Neh. 9:6)?

The truth that God is the creator of all is related to the truth that He alone is the Lord. As the creator, God is a person. And all created beings are responsible to know God and worship Him (Col. 1:16; Rev. 4:11). The "host of heaven" (Neh. 9:6) worships God. They know He is the Person Who created them and everything else in Heaven and the earth, sky, and sea. And they know He preserves, or sustains, all of creation.

God Is Relational and Faithful

Adam and Eve had personal communion with God in the Garden of Eden. They walked and talked with Him and enjoyed fellowshipping with Him. But eventually they sinned and destroyed their fellowship with God (Gen. 3). As a result, everyone is born a sinner separated from God (Rom. 5:12). Only God could act to allow humanity to fellowship with Him again. God's actions required a plan of redemption. That plan began to come to fruition when God chose Abram and made promises to him.

The Levites' prayer expectedly turned to the topic of the call of Abram (Neh. 9:7). He marked their beginning as a nation. God promised Abram that He would make of him a great nation and give that nation a land. He also promised that through Abram all the nations of the earth would be blessed (Gen. 12:1–3). The nations of the earth were indeed blessed when Jesus, God's Son and descendant of Abraham, came to earth and died on the cross for the sins of the world (Rom. 5:17–21).

God did not leave humanity without hope. God loves people, so He gave His Son to die on the behalf of each individual person (John 3:16). All who trust in Christ's death on the cross as the payment for their sins will receive eternal life.

God is not an impersonal distant force. God reached down to humanity and gave His best—His Son—to provide a way for humanity to have a restored relationship with Him.

God's specific relationship to Israel could be summarized with one word: faithful. The Levites' prayer echoed God's faithfulness to their ancestors. At the same time, they recounted how unfaithful their nation had been throughout its history.

5. Read Nehemiah 9:8. In what terms did the Levites note God's faithfulness?

God is still faithful to keep His promises and to stay true to His character. We, like the Israelites, can count on God to be faithful.

God Is Righteous and Just

God is faithful because He is righteous (9:8). God can only do that which is right and according to His holy character. That was comforting to Israel, but it was also a warning. God's righteousness, or justice, demands that He must do what is right as He judges humanity. God cannot ignore sin or excuse it. His justice demands that He judge sin.

6. Read Nehemiah 9:33–35. What did the Levites conclude when they thought about all the trouble that God had brought on them?

As believers, we can have forgiveness of sins even though God is just. God's justice is satisfied by Christ's death on the cross (Rom. 3:21–26). If we confess our sins, God is faithful and right (just) to forgive us our sins and cleanse us; Christ's death on the cross satisfied God's just demand that we pay the penalty for our sin (1 John 1:9).

7. How should the righteousness and justice of God impact a believer's life?

God Is Gracious and Loving

God faithfully gave to Israel throughout her history. The Levites recognized that and listed many of the benefits their nation received by virtue of being God's people.

8. Read Nehemiah 9:7–27. Mark all the times God gave something or someone in the passage. On what basis did God *give* to Israel?

Never once in the Levites' prayer did they list a blessing from God as payment for something Israel had done. They deserved none of the blessings they received from God. But He graciously gave them the blessings anyway.

Every person receives God's grace every day. Air to breathe and food to eat are measures of God's grace. Most people are oblivious to what God gives them. Some have the audacity to complain that they don't have more.

God's love is what motivates His gracious giving.

9. Read Jeremiah 31:3. What are some characteristics of an everlasting love?

God's love is beyond our comprehension. The apostle Paul used several word pictures to try to help us understand how deep God's love is for us.

10. Read Romans 8:38, 39. What impresses you the most about the limitlessness of God's *love*?

As believers on this side of the cross, we understand what it means for the love of God to be "in Christ Jesus our Lord" (Rom. 8:39). Sending His Son to the cross to die for our sins is the ultimate testimony of God's love for us. Salvation that comes because of the cross is the ultimate measure of God's grace.

11. How should the love and grace of God impact a believer's life?

God Is Merciful

While grace is God giving people blessings they don't deserve, mercy is God withholding judgment they do deserve. The Levites repeatedly mentioned God's mercy toward Israel.

12. Read Nehemiah 9:19, 27, 28, 31. What did Israel deserve that God withheld from them?

If Israel got what they deserved, the nation would not exist today. God would have wiped them out long ago. But His mercy is great. It endures forever.

13. Read Lamentations 3:22, 23. Jeremiah wrote this soon after Judah was taken captive by Babylon. What moved God to be merciful and to refrain from consuming His people?

Like the Levites in Nehemiah's day, we should never forget God's mercy toward us.

14. How should God's mercy impact a believer's life?

God Is Patient and Slow to Anger

Alongside God's mercy is His patience and slowness to anger. God in His mercy relieved Israel from oppression by their enemies. By His patience, God testified against Israel and gave the nation opportunities to return to Him (Neh. 9:29, 30). But Israel acted presumptuously and proudly. They did not heed God's commands and sinned against Him instead. They rejected the truth that those who keep God's commands live by them (cf. Lev. 18:5). They shrugged their shoulders and stiffened their necks. They were not going to follow God's commands no matter what. Their actions were childish but serious.

God waited many years for Israel to repent. He sent His prophets, who warned them by the Spirit. At last, God's patience ran out.

15. Read Nehemiah 9:30. How is the "giving" in this verse different from the "giving" in the rest of the passage?

The Levites' prayer purposefully tracks God's gracious giving up to the point of God *giving* Israel into the hands of her enemies. The irony is obvious.

We should not let this lesson escape us. "Slowness to anger" doesn't mean "no anger." God sent His people into captivity for their prolonged rebellion and refusal to hear the Lord. God's patience is a blessing, but it is not a license to continue in sin. God will chasten those He loves and graciously blesses (Heb. 12:5, 6).

16. How should God's patience and slowness to anger impact a believer's life?

At the end of the Levites' prayer, they state the fact that God *gave* the Promised Land to their fathers along with many good things (Neh. 9:35). Yet the Jews are living in the Promised Land as servants (9:36). "Look at us!" they in essence said. "We are servants in the land that God *gave* to our Fathers!"

The Persians controlled the land and forced the Jews to give them the bountiful fruit of the land (9:37). The freedom and control their fathers grasped for in rebellion against God led to their captivity in the Promised Land.

The Levites' prayer ended with a covenant renewal. The history of their nation's unfaithfulness against the backdrop of God's righteousness, justice, grace, love, mercy, patience, and slowness to anger motivated them to respond to God. No doubt they thought about what might have been had their fathers done the same.

17. What does your life reveal about what you actually believe about God's actions? Prayerfully consider this question.

18. Review questions 7, 11, 14, and 16. Which of the responses to God's person are true of your life? Which are not?

19. What might be some consequences of ignoring or dismissing how God relates to you?

20. What steps will you take to adjust your beliefs about God?

God Redeems

▶ Scripture Focus

Matt. 15:3–14; Rom. 2:17–29; 3:9–25; 5:6–9; 6:1–19

Theme

God provided redemption to hopelessly lost, sinful humanity.

Memory Verse

"Therefore we are buried with him by baptism into death: that like as Christ was raised up from the dead by the glory of the Father, even so we also should walk in newness of life" (Romans 6:4).

GETTING STARTED

"Are you comfortable with this?" That question comes up in a plethora of circumstances. We have put a premium on our comfort levels in our culture today. So much so that we tend to see our comfort levels as the lines that divide right from wrong.

1. Why might a believer become comfortable with some sins?

2. How would you describe God's comfort level with sin?

All of us have sins we are more comfortable with than others. While we might think our comfort level with sin is okay, God's comfort level is the one that matters. This lesson will help us adopt God's zero tolerance for sin.

The last session left off with the remnant of Jews in the Promised Land renewing their covenant with God. They fully intended on serving Him faithfully in response to His faithfulness to them. But eventually they proved unfaithful.

Over the next four hundred years they went from under Persian control to under Greek control to a period of self-rule and finally to a period of Roman rule. The Romans ruled the Jews during the time of the New Testament.

Religiously, the Jews developed a system based on strict adherence to both the law of Moses and their traditions. The Pharisees, Sadducees, and scribes led the Jewish religious system. The Jews and their leaders believed others perceived them as pleasing to God. But Jesus Christ and the apostle Paul both made clear that the Jews weren't pleasing to God. They didn't even appear pleasing to God.

The Jews needed to understand the reality of sin and redemption. Jesus showed them the reality of their sin and provided for their redemption. Later, in a letter to the Romans, the apostle Paul wrote clearly about the reality of the Jews' sin and Christ's provision of redemption.

Humanity Is Hopelessly Lost

Many people live with a false view of who they are in relation to God. They think they are basically good and therefore in good standing with God. They believe that while they have not done all they could to deserve Heaven, they certainly have not done enough bad to deserve Hell. That is a dangerous belief.

The need for understanding the reality of sin and redemption is vital to breaking through such self-deception.

Paul addressed the Jews specifically in his letter to the Romans. Though the book was written about two decades after Christ, most Jews were still convinced of their good standing with God.

3. Read Romans 2:17, 18. On what did the Jews rest when they considered their eternal state?

"Privileged" is an accurate word to describe the Jews. God chose them from all nations to be His people. And even though the Jews in Paul's day were living under Roman rule, they still considered themselves to be better than the rest of the world. They let the privilege of being God's people go to their heads. They lost track of reality.

Trying to keep the law should have revealed to the Jews just how sinful they were. But instead, they used the law to prove how righteous they were. They believed they were spiritual leaders for those who did not know God (2:19). And they believed they showed the light of "truth" to the spiritually blind. They used the embodiment of the truth in the law to instruct the foolish and the immature (2:20).

4. Read Romans 2:21–23. What did the Jewish leaders fail to do with the law?

The Jewish leaders developed a system of rules, or traditions, that they added to the law. They even gave the traditions preeminence over the law (Matt. 15:3–6). They used their traditions to carefully craft a system that allowed them to declare themselves righteous for following their rules.

5. Read Matthew 15:3–9. What motivated the Pharisees to write their own traditions?

Paul made it clear that the Pharisees were not actually keeping the law. His series of questions (Rom. 2:21–23) pointed out that the Jews were being hypocritical and breaking the law. Paul even went further to say the Jews were blaspheming God's name (2:24; cf. Is. 52:5; Ezek. 36:20). The Gentiles knew the Pharisees in particular were sinning. They recognized the Pharisees' conniving. The Pharisees' feigned spirituality gave God a bad name among the Gentiles.

6. Read Matthew 15:10–14. What did Christ say about how successful the Pharisees were at leading the spiritually blind?

Paul went on to make the distinction between outward religion and the inward reality of a personal relationship with Christ (2:25–29). What makes a Jew acceptable to God is not outward keeping of rules but an inward circumcision of the heart. In other words, no one, not even the highly privileged Jews, could save themselves by being good and following rules. Salvation comes from God, not from within.

Humanity Needs God's Intervention

7. Read Romans 3:9–18. What did Paul note about humanity's character (vv. 10–12), their speech (vv. 13, 14), and their conduct (vv. 15–18)?

Paul's message is emphatic. All of humanity is hopeless without God's intervention on their behalf. That is reality.

8. Why is it significant that Paul quoted from the Old Testament (Ps. 14:1–3; 53:1–3; Isa. 59:7, 8; et al.) to build his case about the universal sinfulness of humanity?

Paul wrote that the purpose of the law is to show humanity their sinfulness (Rom. 3:19, 20). The mouth of those who say otherwise is stopped by the law. No one could defend himself before God and win the case that he is innocent of sin and worthy of eternal life based on his works. "By the law is the knowledge of sin" (3:20) for every single person.

Where does this leave humanity? Helpless! Humanity needs God's intervention.

Christ Paid the Penalty of Sin

The previous study covered Christ's death on our behalf. The rest of this study will cover God's redemption of humanity in more detail.

God intervened to help humanity by revealing His righteousness. God's righteousness is His absolute perfection, His holiness. His righteousness is "without the law" (3:21). That means it does not come by keeping the law. In fact, the word for "without" is particularly emphatic leaving no doubt that the law cannot bring righteousness.

But God's righteousness was "witnessed" by the law and prophets in that the Old Testament offerings and sacrifices spoke of God's righteousness being given to people. Abraham, for example, had God's righteousness (4:3; cf. Gen. 15:6). Yet even for Abraham, who preceded the law, works was not the means of securing God's righteousness (Rom. 4:1–4).

9. Read Romans 3:22. What is the only means of attaining the righteousness of God?

Since everyone is a sinner and falls short of God's perfection, there is no difference between any two people (3:23). They all must put their faith in Jesus Christ. When they do, God justifies them freely by His grace (3:24). To be justified means to be declared righteous by God. A believer's account in Heaven is wiped clean when God justifies him. Christ's righteousness goes on his account instead.

Believers can have Christ's righteousness credited to their account because of the "redemption" that is in Christ Jesus (3:24). Redemption speaks to a deliverance that is the result of the payment of a price. Christ's shed blood was the price.

God set forth Christ as the propitiation for sin (3:25). "Propitiation" means "acceptable sacrifice." Christ met the requirement that God's holiness be satisfied. In addition, the penalty for sin was canceled by Christ's death on the cross. The believer stands guiltless before God as righteous.

The fact that God "set forth" (3:25) Christ Jesus should not be overlooked. God acted in His love for humanity when He provided a means for salvation. God reached out to man and not the other way around.

10. Read Romans 5:6–8. How would you describe God's love based on this passage?

We should never think that we are somehow special and deserving of salvation. We are worthless beings! Paul made that abundantly clear in Romans 3:10–18. No person would give the life of his son for a repulsive, hateful enemy. Yet that is what God did in providing salvation for us.

As a result of our justification, God's wrath is satisfied (5:9). That wrath would have meant eternal, excruciating torment for us. Being free from that wrath should cause us to rejoice greatly every day. But taking for granted our freedom from God's wrath is easy to do. If we are not careful, we could treat our salvation as if it were ho-hum and old news.

Redemption is a reality we ought to remember and cherish. There could never be a greater cause for rejoicing!

11. How often do you contemplate the value of being redeemed and no longer under the wrath of God?

Christ Assured Victory by His Resurrection

Redemption would not be possible without the resurrection of Christ. Paul continued his letter to the Romans with a section on the resurrection.

Some of the Roman believers thought that since they were justified, they didn't need to worry about obedience to God. They thought that the more they sinned, the greater they made God's grace appear. They asked whether they should continue in sin so grace might abound. Paul answered emphatically with a phrase meaning "God forbid!" (6:1, 2).

As believers, we have died to sin (6:2). That means we are no longer obligated to obey it. We don't have to sin. When we do sin, we are choosing to do so. At salvation, we are identified, or "baptized," with Christ in His death, burial, and resurrection (6:3, 4). Our old relationship with sin has changed. We are no longer slaves to sin. Instead we should "walk in newness of life." Obedience, not sin, should characterize our life after salvation.

The death and resurrection of Christ provide us with this break from sin and the opportunity to live obediently. This break from sin is possible because our old man, our sin nature, was crucified with Christ and "destroyed" (6:5, 6). The word "destroyed" means "rendered powerless" or "made inoperative." Our sin nature no longer automatically controls our lives. We are freed from sin's possession of us (6:7).

Victory over sin is secured because Christ's resurrection brought victory over death once and for all (6:8–10). Christ will never need to die again. His victory over death becomes our victory over death once we put our trust in Him for salvation. We can have eternal life because Christ rose from the dead.

12. Read Romans 6:11, 12. What reality does Paul command us to recognize?

13. What might be some consequences of failing to recognize we are dead to sin?

Victory over sin is not automatic. There is a battle that ensues as we seek to obey God. It means yielding to God daily, presenting our bodies to Him as instruments of righteousness (6:13). It is not about us trying to keep a bunch of rules. Change comes by God's grace (6:14). He enables us to live for Him. That means we need to develop a dependence on God.

14. Why is it important to know that victory over sin comes through God's grace rather than through our own efforts?

We need to think of ourselves as slaves of righteousness with an obligation to obey God. So we should be presenting our bodies to God as instruments for Him to use (6:17–19).

15. What are some practical ways to present our bodies to God as instruments of righteousness?

All of us are affected equally by sin, and none of us can do anything on our own about our sin problem. The reality of redemption is that God sent forth Christ as the acceptable payment for our sin. When we trust in Christ's death on the cross as sufficient for our sins, God declares us righteous. We then can live for God by His grace as we yield ourselves to Him for His use.

MAKING IT PERSONAL

While we may have a Biblical understanding of our sinfulness, our practice may not reflect such an understanding. Some believers will tolerate sin in their lives, thinking they are basically good because they are better than most other people. They don't commit major sins and their reputation is fairly spotless. They settle into life as if God is okay with their sins as long as the sins don't get out of hand. But they are not living according to reality. God is never okay with sin.

16. What sins might people list as minor? What sins might they list as major? Which ones would they list as extreme?

17. What might cause you to become more comfortable with increasingly serious sins?

18. Have you become comfortable with your sin? Do you have a "line" that you won't cross when it comes to the types of sins you are comfortable with? Explain.

19. How might you lower your comfort level to the point of being uncomfortable with any sin in your life? Add to the following ideas.
    - Renew your mind with daily doses of God's Word.
    - Memorize God's Word and use it to combat temptation.
    - Reckon yourself to be dead to sin.
    - Actively look for ways to use your body to serve God.
    - Continue to get to know God's character and ways.

20. When was the last time you took a moment to reflect on your redemption? Has your salvation become ho-hum to you? Spend time every day praising God for your redemption.

Christ Intercedes

▶ Scripture Focus

Luke 22:39–44; Heb. 2:17, 18; 4:14–16; 7:3–28; 12:1–3; James 4:6–10

Theme

Christ, our great high priest, intercedes for us at God's right hand.

Memory Verses

"For we have not an high priest which cannot be touched with the feeling of our infirmities; but was in all points tempted like as we are, yet without sin. Let us therefore come boldly unto the throne of grace, that we may obtain mercy, and find grace to help in time of need" (Hebrews 4:15, 16).

GETTING STARTED

The time between calling 911 and arrival of help can be quite scary, especially if there is a desperate medical emergency or a thief is prowling around your house. But what a relief when the help does arrive!

1. If you could transport one person to your side to help you instantly just by calling his number, whose number would you call?

2. Who might want to call you for your instant help?

Calling 911 doesn't provide instantaneous help, but there is Someone Who is always ready to assist us at a moment's notice. Jesus Christ, our great high priest, is seated in Heaven and is working on our behalf. This study will help you understand His position and the instant assistance He offers you.

The previous study presented the reality of sin and redemption. Christ paid the price for our salvation that we might have His righteousness credited to our account. Christ's work on the cross is complete. There is no further work that needs to be completed in order to secure our salvation. But the cross was just the beginning of Christ's work on our behalf. He is our great high priest seated in Heaven interceding for us before the Father.

Some believers are unaware of Christ's work as their great high priest. Consequently, their spiritual lives are deficient and weak. The book of Hebrews expounds on the high priestly ministry of Jesus. It is the Scripture focus for this lesson.

Our Great High Priest Is Merciful and Faithful

Hebrews 5:1 gives the requirement that priests be taken from among men. So Jesus needed to become a human in order to serve as the great high priest for humanity. Jesus is indeed made "in all things . . . like unto his brethren" (Heb. 2:17). He is lacking nothing that would make Him less than human. The placement of "in all things" at the beginning of the sentence gives the phrase emphasis in the original language, underscoring the completeness of Jesus' humanity. Jesus' humanity, then, allows Him to be a "merciful . . . high priest" (2:17).

As a merciful priest, Jesus fully understands humans. He experienced the full range of temptation and suffering that humans experience, though His experience was far more intense than any other person's experience. The temptation and suffering He faced as He approached the cross could never be equaled.

3. Read Luke 22:39–44. Describe the intense temptation Jesus endured as He faced the cross.

Because of His personal identification with suffering and temptation, Jesus responds compassionately to believers who ask for help. He "is able to succour them that are tempted" (2:18). "Succour" is a rich word in the original language. It comes from two root words meaning "a cry" and "to run." So it conveys the idea of running to aid at the sound of a cry. A parent dropping everything to run to his child at the sound of his child's cry is the picture.

4. How does the illustration of a parent running to the aid of a child help you understand the mercy with which Jesus intercedes for you?

The work of removing our sin by Christ's work on the cross (2:17) gives us access to the Father in the first place. So Christ removed our sin and now stands as our tender, merciful intercessor before the Father.

While "merciful" describes Jesus' intercession on our behalf, "faithful" (2:17) describes His work in relation to the Father. Jesus was faithful in His obedience to the Father in atoning for our sins. As a result, He is able to be faithful in His mercifulness toward us. He will never stop being merciful. "Faithful" is the key word to describe God in the Old Testament, as we saw in lessons 2 and 3. And it is the appropriate word to describe God the Son's intercessory ministry today.

5. What does it mean to you to know that Jesus will always be faithful in His intercessory ministry on your behalf?

Our Great High Priest Provides Access to the Father

The writer of Hebrews picks up the great high priest theme again in chapter 4. His message builds on what he had already written in chapter 2.

Hebrews was most likely written in the final years before the destruction of Jerusalem. Being a Jewish believer was especially difficult during that time. Both the non-believing Jews and the Romans did not want them around. So persecution was on the rise. Staying true to the Lord grew harder and harder. The Jewish believers were tempted to revert back to the Judaism God had saved them from.

The message from the writer is clear. Don't give up! "Hold fast" your "profession" of faith because Jesus passed through the Heavens (4:14).

This is a reference to Jesus' death on behalf of humanity. He provided the final, once-for-all atonement for sin. The Jews needed to reject the notion of returning to a religion that relied on priestly service and sacrifices. Jesus made the need for additional atonement for sin unnecessary when He passed through the heavens and gave every believer access to God.

The writer continued with his words of instruction and encouragement by describing Jesus as the sympathetic high priest (4:15). Jesus understood what the Jewish believers were going through. He had successfully faced tremendous temptation.

6. Read Hebrews 4:15. Evaluate this statement: Successfully resisting temptation allowed Jesus to fully experience how powerful temptation is.

There were no temptations the Jewish readers were experiencing that Jesus hadn't experienced. He was tempted "in all points" (4:15). He couldn't be a more suited sympathizer with their needs.

Instead of giving up, the Jewish readers were to go to the throne of grace to get the "mercy" and "grace" they needed (4:16). Prayer is the means to approaching the throne of grace. "Grace" is God's enabling. The Jewish believers needed God's grace to successfully face temptation. God never intended for believers to try to triumph over temptation on their own.

7. Read Hebrews 4:16. Given the truth of this verse, how important is prayer to gaining victory over sin and temptation?

Why do we not go to the throne of grace as often as we should? Often the problem is pride. We don't think we need God's help, so we don't ask for it. Not praying for others is another indication of pride. When we are wrapped up in ourselves, we don't concern ourselves with the needs of others.

8. Read James 4:6–10. What connection did James make between God's enabling grace and humility?

Our Great High Priest Intercedes Continually

As further evidence for not returning to Judaism, the writer of Hebrews developed the superiority of Christ's priesthood in chapter 7. The comparison of Christ to the levitical priesthood reveals that Christ's high priestly ministry has no end.

Christ was not a descendant of the tribe of Levi. He was instead after the priestly order of Melchizedek. Melchizedek was a priest without a genealogy and without a known beginning or end (7:3). He therefore remained a priest continually. Abraham paid tithes to Melchizedek, as did Levi by virtue of still being in Abraham's loins (7:4–10). This means the levitical priesthood recognized the superiority of the order of Melchizedek.

The levitical priesthood was inherently tied to the law. Since no one could be made perfect by the law, the priesthood connected to the law needed to change if the problem of sin was to be permanently dealt with (7:11, 12, 18, 19). Christ, Who is after the order of Melchizedek, is the answer to the flawed priesthood and law (7:13–17). Unlike the temporary levitical priests, Christ's priesthood lasts forever (7:17). We are able to draw near to God through Christ's continuing high priestly ministry (7:19).

Furthermore, Christ's priestly ministry began by God's oath rather than by a commandment (7:20–22). The oath makes Christ's priesthood superior to that of the levitical priesthood. It also sets Christ up as the guarantee of a better covenant than the Old Testament could sustain. Because Christ is flawless, He can guarantee a better relationship between God and humanity (7:22). We enjoy personal fellowship with God without the need for sacrifices and priests.

The continuous nature of Christ's priesthood is important. Because it is eternal (7:23, 24), Christ is able to save "to the uttermost" those who come to God through Him (7:25). Salvation is forever secure because Christ's priestly ministry is eternal.

9. Read Hebrews 7:25. How would your Christian life be affected if you weren't sure if your salvation was secure?

Jesus' priestly ministry is also continuous for all believers. Christ always lives to make intercession for us (7:25).

10. How should believers respond to Christ's continuous intercessory ministry on their behalf?

11. Read Hebrews 7:26. What made Christ the fitting sacrifice for us?

Because Christ was the perfect sacrifice (7:26), He does not need to daily offer up sacrifices as the levitical priests did. He paid for sins once for all "when He offered up himself" (7:27).

As our sacrifice, Christ is "consecrated," or "perfected," forever (7:28). He stands in contrast to the levitical priests who had "infirmity," a reference to their sinfulness and mortality. Christ completed His mission in offering Himself up as the perfect sacrifice. He is the perfect high priest forever. There could never be a time when Christ could fail as our great high priest.

Our Great High Priest Is Our Example

Christ, our great high priest Who is perfected forever (7:28), is also our example of persevering in obedience. So Christ's intercessory ministry is more than a safety valve for us to use when we need help. His intercession on our behalf and His life of obedience demand that we actively obey and serve Him. He offered Himself up so we might be brought to glory (2:10–18). For now, the process of being brought to glory is called sanctification. Eventually we will be fully sanctified when we are glorified at the coming of Christ (1 Cor. 15:50–53).

The writer of Hebrews opens chapter 12 with the word "wherefore," a link to the previous chapter. Hebrews 11 lists the heroes of the faith—men and women who demonstrated how faith can endure in the face of great challenges. But Christ is the ultimate example of endurance (12:2). As we look to Him, we ought to lay aside sin (12:1).

12. Read Hebrews 12:1. Why is "weight" a good description of our sin?

We are to look to Christ, the "author" and "finisher" of our faith (12:2). "To look" means having eyes for no one but Christ and trusting Him completely. He is to be the central focus of our purpose and course for life. In essence, looking to Jesus is living in the real. When our eyes are fixed on Him, we aren't creating our own reality.

As we consider Christ's role as the great high priest, He made our salvation possible as the "author," and then provided the means for completing our race as the "finisher." As we run, we can know that Christ will enable us to endure.

Jesus endured as He looked forward to the joy set before Him (12:2). His role as the great high priest interceding for us was part of that joy He looked forward to. His joy also included accomplishing the Father's will and presenting believers to the Father as redeemed.

Joy awaits believers who endure in this life. Our future joy will be fully realized in Heaven, but that doesn't mean we can't enjoy life in Christ now. Enduring in our race brings us joy along the way even when we face difficult circumstances.

13. Read Hebrews 12:3. What will considering Christ's endurance do for believers?

When we do get discouraged and think about giving up, we need to consider the hostility that Christ endured (12:3). Doing so will strengthen us for the way.

The invitation to approach the throne of grace based on Christ's high priestly role is compelling. But simply feeling compelled to pray is worthless. We must turn the compelling feeling into action.

14. Why might believers reject Christ's invitation to the throne of grace?
   SUDDEN, FREQUENT, CONSISTENT

MAKING IT PERSONAL

15. What three words would you use to describe your prayer life?

16. What does the amount of time you spend in prayer say about what you think about yourself?

It is easy to be fooled by Satan into thinking we don't need to pray. The "normalness" or our lives lulls us into a pattern of self-sufficiency. But when we suddenly face the reality of difficult circumstances, we quickly understand we should have been praying all along.

17. How does an awareness of Jesus' high priestly ministry affect your motivation to pray?

18. What will you do to strengthen your prayer life?

Perhaps the first step to strengthen your prayer life is to pray about your prayer life. Praying is a spiritual discipline that requires God's enabling grace. He will help you become consistent and real in your prayer life if you will simply ask!

The Holy Spirit Empowers

▶ Scripture Focus

John 16:5–7; Rom. 8:9, 26, 27; 12:1, 2; 1 Cor. 6:17–20; 12:11; Gal. 5:16, 22–24; Eph. 4:30; 5:18; Phil. 4:7

Theme

God gives us the Holy Spirit to empower us to live for Him.

Memory Verse

"Nevertheless I tell you the truth;
It is expedient for you that I go away: for if I go not away,
the Comforter will not come unto you;
but if I depart, I will send him unto you" (John 16:7).

GETTING STARTED

Most people don't feel comfortable in front of a camera, though some do and act like fourth graders when it is rolling. Those people are in the minority. As many as three-fourths of women and half of men are "camera shy."

1. How do you respond when someone has a camera rolling?

2. How might having a camera follow you around be like having the Holy Spirit inside you?

Though the Holy Spirit is with us as believers, we often completely ignore Him as if He doesn't really exist. This lesson will help us understand and rightly respond to the Biblical reality of the Holy Spirit.

Christ's redemption and high priestly ministry were the focuses of lessons four and five. Christ's redeeming death and resurrection paved the way for His high priestly ministry. This study focuses on God's ministry on earth in the person of the Holy Spirit. The coming of the Holy Spirit is another benefit from Christ's redemptive work. The Holy Spirit works in tandem with Jesus Christ to enable believers to serve God and to gain victory over temptation.

The Holy Spirit Is a Real Person

3. How often do you consider the fact that the Holy Spirit is a person? What difference has that fact made in your life?

The Scriptures leave no doubt that the Holy Spirit is a person. According to the Bible, He has an obvious intellect, emotion, and will. In Paul's letter to the Romans, he ascribed emotion to the Holy Spirit (Rom. 8:26). When we are not sure either what to pray or what more we could say to God, the Holy Spirit makes intercession for us "with groanings which cannot be uttered." The "groanings" are inaudible sighs. The sighs convey the Holy Spirit's emotional response to our circumstances. He feels the weight of both our continuous state of feebleness and our times of suffering.

4. Read Romans 8:26. How should we respond to Holy Spirit's emotional response to us?

The apostle Paul then talked about "the mind of the Spirit" (Rom. 8:27). With a mind, the Spirit possesses intellect and is capable of knowing and thinking. God knows what the Spirit is thinking as the Spirit is groaning and interceding on behalf of believers.

The Holy Spirit is also able to make decisions because He has a will. In Paul's letter to the church at Corinth he wrote about the Holy Spirit distributing spiritual gifts "as he will" (1 Cor. 12:11).

Most believers would readily agree that the Holy Spirit is real. But many act as if He is not. An awareness of the Holy Spirit in our lives as a living person is vital to being who God wants us to be.

The Spirit Indwells Every Believer

The importance of knowing the Spirit is a person grows when we consider He indwells every believer (Rom. 8:9). We all have the person of the Holy Spirit in us. That should cause us to want to know all we can about Him and His ministry on our behalf.

5. What thoughts go through your mind when you consider the person of the Holy Spirit is dwelling in you?

In the hours before His arrest and eventual death, Christ told His disciples that He would be leaving them (John 16:5). That sounded like bad news. The disciples even had sorrow fill their hearts as Christ talked to them (16:6).

6. Read John 16:7. How did Jesus characterize His leaving?

Why is it such good news to have Christ in Heaven instead of on earth? Christ, God with us (Emmanuel), left so that the Holy Spirit, God in us, could come (16:7). The fact that Christ is now acting as our great high priest in Heaven makes the transition from "Christ with us" to the "Spirit in us" even more wonderful for all believers.

The Spirit Motivates

God intends for us to live with an awareness of the reality of the Spirit's presence in us. Paul instructed the Ephesian believers to put away sins such as lying, sinful anger, stealing, speaking corruptly, and reacting bitterly (Eph. 4:25–29, 31). They had to put away the sins in order to "grieve not the holy Spirit of God" (4:30). This is more evidence that the Spirit is not simply an impersonal power or force. He "grieves" when we sin because He is emotionally sensitive to sin.

7.   Read Ephesians 4:30. How might a believer be affected by an awareness of the Spirit's grieving every time he sins?

Knowing the Spirit is with us should motivate us to put off sin. He is God in us. He reads our thoughts like a book and peers through our eyes to see exactly what we see. He goes where we go and hears every word we say, even what we mutter under our breath.

Not "grieving" the Spirit is the negative motivation of the reality of the Spirit in us. Paul's letter to Corinth gave the positive motivation. Knowing the Spirit is in us ought to motivate us to want to glorify God (1 Cor. 6:17–19). Our bodies are the "temple" of the Holy Spirit. So what we do with our bodies should bring glory to God (6:20). "Glorify" has the idea of making large or magnifying. In other words, people should be able to see God in us and learn about God from watching our lives.

8.   What do you suppose the Spirit is thinking when you are in the midst of a particularly demanding act of service for the Lord?

9.   How should the Spirit's thoughts about your sacrificial service for God shape your attitude as you serve?

Consider how the world would be different if believers grasped the reality of the Spirit in them and said, "I want to glorify God with my body and make the Holy Spirit glad to be in me!"

The Spirit Offers Power through Yieldedness

The Holy Spirit not only motivates change, but He also facilitates change. How do we make sure the power of the Holy Spirit is in gear in our lives and that we are not idling or trying to coast along under our own strength? It takes both devotion and dependence.

Everyone is devoted to someone or something. Romans 12:1 calls for devotion to God. Paul's appeal for devotion is based on "the mercies of God." These mercies include our justification, redemption, victory over sin, no condemnation or separation, and eternal life—all topics Paul spelled out in Romans 1–11.

We are to present our "bodies" to God, a reference to our entire lives, including our activities and ambitions. We "present" our lives to God by yielding to Him. Our will becomes subject to God's will. We live for Him.

10. Why is yielding yourself to God a "reasonable" service (Rom. 12:1)? Consider the Biblical realities you have learned about in this study.

Yielding ourselves to God is not a onetime decision. We must daily decide to devote ourselves to God and live in a state of "yieldedness." We must also have our minds transformed from a sinful, selfish mind-set to a selfless, godly mind-set.

Lesson 1 dealt with the transformation of the mind. That lesson presented mind transformation as related to putting on the "armor of light" (Rom. 13:12). The belt of truth and the sword of the Spirit are both vital in mind transformation (Eph. 6:14, 17). When we learn the truth of God's Word on a daily basis, it becomes our offensive weapon against living a self-absorbed life that is directed by our own will. Instead of this selfish life, we "prove," or learn by experience, that God's will is "good," "acceptable, and perfect" (Rom. 12:2). "Acceptable" means "pleasing." As we do God's will, we will find satisfaction and joy in life. "Perfect" refers to the fact that God's will encompasses all of life.

Our "yieldedness" engages the Spirit to be active in our lives. That is the first ingredient in activating the Spirit. The second ingredient is our humble dependence on the Spirit.

The Spirit Offers Power through Dependence

Galatians 5:16 tells us to "walk in the Spirit." Our "walk" refers to our lives—who we are and what we do. We are to live "in," or "by," the Spirit. Living by the Spirit means depending on Him.

11. Read Galatians 5:16. What will happen to those who walk in the Spirit?

We will get nowhere in our Christian walk if we depend on ourselves. We might have some superficial victories, but we will ultimately be defeated and discouraged.

Remember the discussion about our flesh back in lesson one. Our flesh wants us to live in dreamland. It demands control of our lives and will create false realities. Living in dependence on the Spirit is the way to render our flesh dead. Galatians 5:24 says, "They that are Christ's have crucified the flesh with the affections and lusts." We don't have to live according to a false reality. We can live victoriously by the Spirit.

The message of Ephesians 5:18 is one of dependence on the Holy Spirit too. It says to be "filled" with the Spirit. To be filled with the Spirit means to be controlled by the Spirit. The verb tense actually communicates an ongoing filling of the Spirit. We are filled by the Spirit as we lean on Him for power and direction.

12. Why would Paul couple the command to be filled with the Spirit with a command not to be drunk? What is the connection?

The Spirit Produces Godly Character

Yielding to the Spirit and living dependent on Him unleashes the Spirit's power in our lives. Once the Spirit's power is unleashed, it begins to show in our lives in the form of "fruit." That fruit is seen in godly character and effective service.

13. When we depend on the Spirit, we "bear fruit." What do we learn from the fruit-bearing metaphor?

Galatians 5:22 and 23 list the fruit of the Spirit. If we are living Spirit-controlled lives, then the fruit in the passage will be characteristic of our lives.

Love, joy, and peace are the first three characteristics listed as evidence of a Spirit-filled life (Gal. 5:22). All of them have to do with our relationship with God. "Love" is listed first because all of the other characteristics come from it. This type of love is divine and therefore pure. It is unadulterated with selfish motives or lust.

"Joy" is the inward satisfaction no matter what circumstances we face. It is more than happiness, which comes and goes depending on what happens to us. Joy does not make sense to those living in the flesh. It defies logic.

"Peace" is similar to joy. It, too, remains despite circumstances. It results in a settled heart and mind free from worry (Phil. 4:7).

14. Read Philippians 4:7. When have you experienced the peace of God that "passes all understanding"?

The next three characteristics are evident in our relationships with others (Gal. 5:22). A person who is "longsuffering" will not retaliate or seek revenge when wronged. Instead he will bear with a person and seek reconciliation and solutions. This does not mean he rolls over and lets people walk all over him. But it does mean he will not be motivated by a selfish desire to defend his rights at all costs.

15. How might long-suffering be evident in your life as you travel down a busy highway?

Instead of seeking revenge, the Spirit-controlled person will show "gentleness" and "goodness" to others instead. That's not natural! We need the Holy Spirit to respond to hateful or rude people with kindness and goodness.

16. How might a hateful person respond when you show him gentleness and goodness instead of revenge?

The last three characteristics are inward fruit (5:22b, 23). "Faith" refers to "faithfulness." We are dependable people when we are led by the

Spirit. Some people think that being irresponsible is okay as long as we don't mean to hurt anyone by it.

17. Why is God concerned about whether we are faithful and dependable?

A person showing "meekness" is not demanding. He uses his power with wisdom and grace. "Temperance" is "self-control." A temperate person does not fly into a rage. Nor does he act based on lusts.

It is tempting to see a list of characteristics and use them as a means to prove we are controlled by the Spirit. But they are "fruit" of the Spirit, not "proof" of the Spirit. The fruit will be real when we learn to devote ourselves to God and depend on His Spirit. If we catch ourselves thinking about how spiritual we are, we are probably pretending to be Spirit led. Pride is a work of the flesh and evidence that the Spirit is not controlling our lives (James 4:6).

The Spirit Produces Effective Service

The fruit of the Spirit is valuable as we strive to serve the Lord. It helps our service be effective. Imagine how ineffective our service would be if we didn't have the fruit of the Spirit.

18. What would happen if we served as loveless, sad, nervous, defensive, mean, undependable, and undisciplined people?

The Holy Spirit oversees the distribution of spiritual gifts to believers as mentioned in the discussion about His personality (1 Cor. 12:11). He is also the One Who works, or energizes, the gifts. So the Spirit directly influences our service and brings results from our efforts. Without the Spirit, our service for the Lord would be superficial and temporary.

19. How much thought have you given to the role of the Holy Spirit in your life?

20. Describe your level of devotion to God. What evidence from your life supports your description?

21. On whom are you depending for strength and direction in life?

Whether the fruit of the Spirit is evident in your life is a clue to your dependence. If there is no fruit in your life, then you aren't depending on the Spirit.

22. Write a statement describing God's expectations of your devotion to Him and your dependence on the Spirit.

23. Review the list of action steps for living in the real. (See question 21 of lesson 1.) Many of these same steps are important in your devotion to God. Record three of those steps you need to take.

God Speaks, Part 1

▶ Scripture Focus

Gen. 3:15; Prov. 2:6–15; Rom. 5:8; Phil. 2:15; 2 Tim. 3:16, 17; Heb. 4:12, 13; 2 Pet. 1:20, 21

Theme

God speaks to humanity through the Bible.

Memory Verse

"For the word of God is quick, and powerful, and sharper than any twoedged sword, piercing even to the dividing asunder of soul and spirit, and of the joints and marrow, and is a discerner of the thoughts and intents of the heart" (Hebrews 4:12).

GETTING STARTED

A truck driver for a cola company pulled into Mount Pleasant, Iowa, to make his delivery. As he pulled up to the address, he was a little confused. When he asked about delivering the cola, the man at the address pointed out that he needed to be in Mount Pleasant, *Michigan*. That is about 350 miles from Mount Pleasant, Iowa. The man was lost and didn't realize it.

1. When have you been lost without even knowing it?

2. What helped you realize you were not on the right road?

This study will help you understand the reality of the Word of God and its value in giving you direction in life.

Some Christians consult the Bible only when they need a lift or when they want inspiration for making a decision. But the Bible is neither a Hallmark card nor a Magic 8 Ball. To treat is as either is insulting to God the Father Who inspired it, the Son Whose story of redemption it contains, and the Spirit Who empowers it. We ought to treat the Bible with the utmost respect, for it is highly valuable. The Bible really is God's Word. That is a Biblical reality we must awake to.

The Bible Is Inspired

Perhaps no doctrine in all of theology is as important as the inspiration of Scripture. If we cannot be sure that the Bible is inspired, then we can't be sure of anything it says. That's why God made it clear in the Scriptures that they are indeed inspired.

The Greek word for "inspiration" (2 Tim. 3:16) literally means "God-breathed." The idea is that the very words of Scripture originated with God. He is the sole source of Scripture.

3.   Read 2 Timothy 3:16a. Why is it important to know that "all" Scripture is inspired by God? Consider the authority of Scripture.

Theological liberals deny the inspiration of Scripture so they can claim authority over the Scriptures. They mold passages to say what they want them to say, or they dismiss passages altogether. This is because they view the Bible as a witness of God instead of the Word of God. Specifically, they focus on what Jesus says about peace, justice, fairness, compassion, and love. They ignore other passages on God's judgment of sin and the Lake of Fire.

Peter wrote about the theological liberals of his day. He warned believers to be wary of the "unlearned and unstable" who take the Scriptures and "wrest," or "twist," them (2 Pet. 3:16). Some even used the Scriptures to satisfy their greed (2:3). "Destruction" was the end for such apostates (3:16). Peter told the believers to "beware" lest they be led away by the same error (3:17). This is the background of Peter's important teaching considering the origin of Scripture (1:20, 21).

4. Read 2 Peter 1:20, 21. What is the clear teaching in this passage concerning the origin of the Scriptures?

The Scriptures are not of "private interpretation" (1:20). "Interpretation" is translated from a word that means "unloosing." The idea is that the Scriptures were not unleashed by any of the human authors. The Scriptures all came from God. So no one has the right to twist the Scriptures by yanking them out of context.

God inspired the Scriptures, but He did not physically write the Scriptures Himself. He used people to write His words. The human authors each wrote from their own personalities and according to their personal styles. So, for example, the apostle Paul's writings are uniquely his, while Peter's are distinctly his. Some people have a hard time getting past that fact. Perhaps it could also be a reason people feel free to use the Scriptures as they wish.

But God purposefully preserved the writers' personalities and styles as they wrote. He wanted them to write with their own personal flavor. When we consider that God gave the writers their personalities, seeing evidence of their personalities in the books they wrote should not be a problem for us. The end result is the inspired Word of God. It is word for word what God intended it to be.

So the God we learned about in lessons two and three wrote a book for us. That is amazing to consider. We should treasure our Bibles.

5. What would constitute treasuring your Bible?

The Bible Is Living and Powerful

Not only is the Bible God's very word, but it is also alive!

6. What do you think of when you hear the Bible is "living"?

The writer of Hebrews called the Word of God "living" (Heb. 4:12). That means God's Word is active in our lives. It makes a difference when we read it and digest it. The Holy Spirit is the One Who makes the Bible active and "powerful." He uses the Scriptures to penetrate our hearts much like a sword would. It cuts to the very core of who we are. It reveals what is real about us. God's Word shows us reality.

The meaning of the division of "soul and spirit" and "joints and marrow" is not particularly clear. But the phrases do point to the degree to which God's Word penetrates who we are as person—nothing is left uncovered.

7. Read Hebrews 4:12. What does the Word of God reveal about a person's heart?

We could hide our attitudes, motivations, and intentions from people. But God's Word always reveals them.

8. Read Hebrews 4:13. To what degree are our lives exposed by God, the author and power behind the Word of God?

The God Who sees all we are uses the Word of God, activated by the Spirit of God, to expose us to the reality of who we are. We should be convicted of any sin in our lives as we read and study God's Word, even sins of attitude, motives, and intentions. But we should also be encouraged by God's offer of forgiveness and the fact that as we serve Him in His power He will one day reward us (4:13).

The Bible is alive! It is astonishing that a believer would ever treat it like just another book or an annoying e-mail. We should cherish it and devour it!

The Bible Is a Loving, Sufficient Message

The Bible is a love letter to humanity. Just imagine the hopeless chaos without the special revelation of the Bible. The love of God is replete throughout the Bible. Beginning in the Garden of Eden, God lovingly provided for Adam and Eve's sins and promised a permanent solution would come (Gen. 3:15). That solution came in the Person of Jesus when God showed His love toward us by sending Christ to die for us (Rom. 5:8).

9. Which of the many passages on God's love are particularly meaningful to you?

10. Read Romans 6:23a. How could Bible passages that speak of eternal judgment be part of God's loving message?

God is clear on the consequences of dying without trusting in Jesus as Savior. He tells us that message to motivate us to share the gospel and to motivate the lost to trust in Christ as their Savior.

Perhaps we could summarize the Bible with the phrase "for God so loved the world" (John 3:16). If we truly appreciate the love of God, then we ought to be concerned about what He in His love has revealed to us in His Word.

The Bible Is a Sufficient Message

God in His love made the Bible sufficient for us. There is nothing lacking. God didn't forget to add a section. It is perfect and complete.

Studies like this one help you understand the Bible, but the power for a course like this comes from God's Word. As a matter of principle, we as believers ought to choose Bible study materials that are centered around God's Word rather than around a particular personality or philosophy. Some popular writers might make us feel better or believe we can handle life more effectively, but popular writing alone will have little effect on our lives or on eternity.

The apostle Paul wrote to a pastor named Timothy about the sufficiency of the Word of God (2 Tim. 3:16, 17). He said all Scripture is "profitable for doctrine, for reproof, for correction, for instruction in righteousness."

"Doctrine" is what the Bible says is right. It is the Bible's teaching oriented toward application. So it is more than heavy systematic theology. It is highly practical too. If we follow the Bible's doctrine, we will stay on the road God has for us. But none of us is perfect. All of us eventually leave the road to drive into the wilderness. Even the apostle Paul admitted his struggle to stay on the road (Rom. 7:14–23).

As we begin to drive into the wilderness, the Bible will give us "reproof" to show us where we have gone wrong (2 Tim. 3:16). Sometimes God uses a pastor's message or a challenge from a friend to reprove us with His Word. Other times it comes as we read or study God's Word for ourselves. And if we have memorized God's Word, the Holy Spirit will use those verses to reprove us.

11. What means has God used to reprove you and show you your sin?

"Reproof" is not an end in itself. "Correction" is needed to point the way back to the road God wants us to be on. The word "correction" comes from a root word meaning to "set up straight" that which is crooked. Solomon talks about the crooked way of the wicked in Proverbs 2:6–15.

12. Read Proverbs 2:6–15. Summarize the description of the path of the wicked.

"Correction" shows us how to get back on the path of the upright. The Epistles in particular are helpful for correction. Ephesians 4:17–24 is a clear "correction" passage. It even uses the walking metaphor. The main passages in lesson one of this course are also passages with "correction" in them (Rom. 13:11–14; 1 Cor. 15:30–34; Eph. 5:3–17).

Philippians 2:15 tells us we are to shine as lights in the midst of the crooked generation around us (cf. Eph. 4:17, 18). The path of the upright is light, while the crooked path of the wicked is "darkness" (Prov. 2:13). As we stay on the path of the upright, we shine the hope of the gospel to the wicked.

"Instruction in righteousness" keeps us on the path of the upright. On the road it serves as the white lines and guardrails. "Instruction" means "training" or "guidance." It is similar to the teaching process a parent takes his child through. In order for us to benefit from "instruction in righteousness," we need to admit we need the training. That takes humility.

The result of doctrine, reproof, correction, and instruction in righteousness is becoming a man of God who is "perfect," or "complete," and "thoroughly furnished unto all good works" (2 Tim. 3:17). In other words, the Bible is a sufficient message. It has all you need to become what God wants you to be.

MAKING IT PERSONAL

13. How would someone describe the value of the Bible based solely on your use of it?

14. How would their description compare to what you know to be true of the Bible's value?

15. What are some reasons believers might give for not valuing the Bible as God's very words?

16. What should characterize your approach to God's Word? Should you just see it as something you are supposed to read? Explain.

17. Based on what you've learned about God's Word, what results would you expect from a concerted, consistent effort to know God's Word?

Be concerted and consistent in your approach to God's Word. Reviewing the lessons and passages in this study book would be a good place to start if you have not been concerted and consistent in your study of God's Word.

God Speaks, Part 2

▶ Scripture Focus

Acts 20:17–35; 1 Cor. 3:3–15; 2 Tim. 2:1, 2; 4:1–5

Theme

God expects us to handle His Word carefully and correctly.

Memory Verse

"Preach the word; be instant in season, out of season; reprove, rebuke, exhort with all longsuffering and doctrine"
(2 Timothy 4:2).

GETTING STARTED

Oops!

That's not something you want to hear when someone is using a hard-to-handle tool like a Weedwhacker or hair trimmer. Once the tulips or the tuft of hair is gone, there is no immediate fix!

1. What are some other tools that are not easy to handle?

2. When have you had trouble with a hard-to-handle tool or machine?

The Bible is a tool that we must be careful to use well. Misusing the Bible can have serious consequences. This lesson focuses on handling the Word of God carefully and correctly.

As we learned in the previous lesson, we ought to value God's Word highly and be concerted and consistent in our study of it. We also need to be faithful in using God's Word correctly.

After the apostle Paul told Timothy the value of God's Word in 2 Timothy 3:16 and 17, he charged him to be true to God's Word (2 Tim. 4:1). The word he used for "charge" is an intensified word showing the earnestness and seriousness of the charge. That charge is as important today as it has ever been. And while Paul's words are primarily written to pastors, the principles about handling God's Word apply to everyone who opens God's Word to study it or teach it. God expects us to handle the Bible carefully and correctly because it really is His word.

Be Ready for Judgment

Paul's charge to Timothy was "before" God and the Lord Jesus Christ. The wording he used meant "in the presence of," a phrase with courtroom implications in that day. So Timothy's case would be drawn up in the presence of his judge, Jesus Christ. Paul is referring to the Judgment Seat of Christ, which will take place in Heaven after the rapture of the church. All believers who are part of the church, including those who have already died, will give a personal account of their lives at the Judgment Seat of Christ (2 Cor. 5:10). Christ will distribute crowns as rewards to those who served Him well. Christ will also assign ruling positions in His millennial Kingdom as rewards (2 Tim. 4:1; Rev. 5:10).

So what will Jesus Christ evaluate when He examines Timothy's ministry of the Word? He will be examining in part whether Timothy based his ministry on the Word and whether he used the Word as God intended.

All ministries are not necessarily based on the Word. They might look successful because the seats are full and the facilities are nice, but Jesus won't judge a ministry based on its appearance. Remember that all things are "naked and opened" (Heb. 4:13) before Christ. This applies to our ministry too. If we don't conduct ministry based on God's Word, then our efforts will be in vain. There are no "best of show" awards in Heaven.

The church at Corinth was building their ministry on personalities. Some said they were of Apollos while other said they were of Paul (1 Cor. 3:3, 4).

This caused a division in the church. Paul addressed the church and pointed out their error.

3. Read 1 Corinthians 3:3, 4. What was the reason for the division?

Paul said the foundation he laid for their ministry was Christ and that they needed to be careful how they built on that foundation (3:10).

4. Read 1 Corinthians 3:11–15. What will happen to a ministry that is built without God and His Word at the center?

If we want our ministry efforts to last for eternity, then we will use God's Word as our ministry guide and depend on it for ministry success.

God will also judge us for how we handled His Word. While Paul was returning from his third missionary journey, he stopped in Miletus to meet the leaders of Ephesus (Acts 20:17). He told them that he believed he would be arrested and chained once he arrived in Jerusalem but that he would not let that deter him from the ministry he received from the Lord (20:22–24). Then he described his ministry to them. He said he was "pure from the blood of all men" (20:26). By this he meant he had been faithful in sharing God's Word. He actually was alluding to the work of a watch-man who had the job of alerting of danger.

5. Read Acts 20:27. Why was Paul confident of his job as a "watchman"?

6. What might cause a church to refrain from declaring the "whole counsel of God"?

Paul went on to give reasons why preaching the whole counsel of God was so important. First, their calling was from God (20: 28). They were overseeing His flock. Second, false teachers would arise from within their church (20:29–31). They needed to be faithful with God's Word to be able to spot the false teachers and prevent them from being an influence. Third, the whole counsel of God builds up believers in the faith (20:32). Who were they to say some of it was not necessary or too controversial?

Paul then gave a personal note. He said he coveted no one's money (20:33–35). No one could accuse Paul of using the Bible and his preaching for financial gain. He even went out of his way to give financial support to the weak (20:35).

7. How concerned have you been with your handling of God's Word?

Focus on the Bible

"Preach the Word!" is Paul's clarion call to Timothy (2 Tim. 4:2). The Bible is our authority, and we must teach it as our authority. God has not promised to work through a ministry that doesn't take the highest view of the Bible. He expects us to have Paul's approach to the Word (Acts 20:27). Teach it all as God intended. Nothing more and nothing less!

You can't go wrong teaching the Bible as authoritative, for it is the catalyst for life change. It cannot be replaced by a strategy, a program, or a leader. The Bible should be our focus and our authority in ministry.

Paul then told Timothy to be ready "in season and out of season" (2 Tim. 2:4). In other words, Timothy was to teach the Bible without compromise even if some of the Bible's teachings weren't popular. He wasn't supposed to base his message on the latest polling data or the wishes of the well-endowed members of his church.

8. What are some Bible truths that are becoming less popular?

When we compromise the Bible in even the slightest ways, we undermine its authority. This includes choosing Bible curriculum that ignores certain doctrines or uses generalizations to allow for different views. When choosing curriculum and other resources, we should evaluate whether it undermines the Bible's authority.

In an age of increasing pressure to teach the Bible in more politically correct and palatable ways, we must not compromise the Bible's message. That includes making sure the church's teaching materials treat the Bible as God intended.

Instead of compromising, we must "reprove, rebuke, exhort with all longsuffering and doctrine" (2 Tim. 4:2). Reproving corrects doctrinal error, rebuking exposes sin and brings a person to repentance, and exhorting encourages godliness. The Bible changes lives, so it ought to be the focus of our ministry rather than a particular author or personality. The fact that Paul gave the benefits of God's Word in both 2 Timothy 3:16 and 17 and 4:2 shows the importance of God's Word when it comes to life change.

9. Why should we be cautious in looking to a particular author or personality for all of our spiritual insight?

Know the Times

Preaching and teaching the Word was so important because of the times Timothy lived in. Some of his students would eventually reject sound doctrine and desire to hear what they wanted to hear instead (2 Tim. 4:3, 4).

10. Read 2 Timothy 4:3. Why will people reject sound doctrine? What will be their motivation?

Rejecting sound doctrines such as a literal, six-day creation and inspiration of Scriptures is a heart problem rather than a head problem. The heart lusts for control. If it is left unchecked, it will revolt against sound doctrine so it might be its own master.

Rejecting doctrine is the same as creating your own reality. Back in lesson one we considered the following reasons why people create their own realities: (1) To be in control of life, (2) to escape responsibility to

God, (3) to gain spiritual recognition without a spiritual commitment, (4) to relieve guilt over sin, and (5) to excuse spiritual indifference and inactivity. All of those reasons for creating a reality require that the person reject Bible doctrine. Our flesh hates doctrine. Those who let their flesh control their lives instead of rendering it dead (Rom. 6:11) will eventually not endure sound doctrine.

So Timothy's day is no different than our own. People still have their flesh, their old nature, that lusts for control. Since that is the case, there will be those believers who leave their flesh unchecked and who eventually won't endure sound doctrine.

11. Read 2 Timothy 4:3b. What will those who won't endure sound doctrine do to appease their flesh?

12. What do you suppose the teachers in 2 Timothy 4:3 think they will gain from "scratching the ears" of their students?

Teachers who compromise doctrine and students who won't endure sound doctrine have a codependent relationship. They both use each other to justify their actions and create what they are convinced is reality.

This pattern is prevalent today. It explains why churches and colleges turn from God and begin to deny doctrines they once held so strongly. The solution is to keep preaching the Word without compromise and for the purpose of changing lives.

Students who won't endure false doctrine will turn from the truth to embrace "fables," or myths (2 Tim. 4:4). In other words, they will reject reality for a lie that suits their lusts. And they will do so proudly as if they are somehow progressive in their thinking and not under such a rigid approach to truth.

13. Read 2 Timothy 4:4. What religious "fables" might be embraced by those who turn from the truth?

The verb "turned unto" (4:4) is a medical term used to describe the wrenching of a joint out of place. So turning to a myth—a false reality—is not what is expected. Those who turn from the truth to myths are "out of joint" spiritually.

All believers have the potential to be wrenched "out of joint" spiritually. We need to be aware of that potential and be watchful.

Be Watchful

As we are aware of the times, we must "watch" for heresy and compromise in our ministries (4:5). The verb "watch" is in the present tense, so the idea is to have a constant state of watchfulness. And the word "watch" in the original language has the connotation of "being sober." We are not to let anything cloud our judgment when it comes to decisions regarding heresy and compromise in our ministries.

14. Why might a church put their guard down when it comes to watching for heresy and compromise in their ministry?

We should consistently evaluate our decisions by asking ourselves questions such as the following: (1) Are we changing the Bible's message to reach attendance or budget goals? (2) Are we purposefully ignoring some doctrines so we don't cause a division in the church? (3) Are we choosing curriculum and other resources without considering its content? (4) Are we allowing people to join the church and minister in leadership positions without interviewing them about their doctrinal beliefs?

As time wears on, teaching and preaching without compromise will become harder. In fact, we should expect persecution in our lifetimes for standing for the truth.

The time is perhaps near when preaching God's Word authoritatively and uncompromisingly will be considered a hate crime. Homosexuality will most likely be the flash point. We should expect to be pressured to change our message. And eventually we should expect to be persecuted if we refuse to accept and approve "alternative" lifestyles. Those ministries that have refused to compromise on the Word will be better equipped to "endure afflictions" (4:5; cf. 2 Tim. 2:3–13).

15. What other issues could become flash points for affliction?

Paul encouraged Timothy to "make full proof" of his service for the Lord, including his work of evangelism (4:5). Timothy was to stick with it all the way to the end. He was not to give up or cower when affliction came.

Paul knew the end of his life was near. He wanted to be certain that his ministry would continue after he was gone. Timothy was an important part of the continuation of Paul's ministry (cf. 1 Tim. 4:12–16). Of course Paul didn't wait until he was about to die before he laid a foundation for the continuation of his ministry. He had worked with Timothy for years to prepare him to minister as a good soldier (2 Tim. 2:1, 2).

16. Read 2 Timothy 2:1, 2. What responsibility does each generation of believers have?

We need to be concerned about the next generation. Are they getting the message of living an uncompromising faith? Will they see the importance of preaching the Word as God intended? Are we settling for "good" kids instead of "godly" kids? If so, we are dooming the next generation.

Our compromises send the message to the next generation that the Bible is not authoritative. As a result, the next generation won't look to the Word of God for their authority.

We need to hold God's Word up high. Preach the WORD as authoritative, present it without compromise, and teach it to change lives!

MAKING IT PERSONAL

17. What message are you sending to the next generation by your handling of God's Word?

18. How watchful of compromise of the truth has your church been?

19. What safeguards against compromise might your church need to put in place? Add to the following list.

    - Use the church doctrinal statement to screen potential members.
    - Teach doctrine regularly.
    - Have a system in place for evaluating curriculum or other program materials.

Pray for your pastor and church leadership that they would have the wisdom to focus on God's Word and use it exactly as God intended.

20. What personal safeguards could keep you from compromising God's Word? Add to the list.

    - Use Bible study helps that are Bible based and that take a strong stand on the authority of Scripture.
    - Avoid self-help books that emphasize finding solutions to problems through self-love and self-actualization.

God Works

▶ Scripture Focus

Various passages

Theme

God works through the church, His program for this age.

Memory Verse

"Obey them that have the rule over you, and submit yourselves: for they watch for your souls, as they that must give account, that they may do it with joy, and not with grief: for that is unprofitable for you" (Hebrews 13:17).

GETTING STARTED

How many uses are there for rubber bands? No one knows, for people are coming up with new uses for them all the time. Some uses are devious. An 18-year old Ukrainian boy developed a battery-operated rubber band machine gun that holds 672 rubber bands and fires 14 a second!

1. What might be some other devious uses for rubber bands?

2. What might Stephen Perry, the first to patent rubber bands, think of people shooting them at each other with rapid force?

Sometimes new uses for inventions, as with rubber bands, aren't so nice. The local church is God's idea. Unfortunately some people have used it in ways God never intended and would never approve. This lesson will examine the reality of church and the vital part it plays in our lives.

The Church Is God's Idea

The local church is God's idea. But what church is to some people is not what God designed it to be. Some believers have made church their club. They like to go and hang out with their friends, but they aren't too interested in the actual work of the church.

3. Read 1 Corinthians 12:4–7. What message do these verses send to those who want to use church as a club?

Other people see church as a runway for drawing attention to themselves. They attend so they can show off their latest outfit or jewelry, brag about their recent vacation, or display their "ride." They are preoccupied with who has what and who went where.

The church at Corinth had turned the Lord's Supper into an opportunity for members to show off their status (1 Cor. 11:18–21). They gathered for a meal before observing the Lord's Supper. Some members brought their large, lavish meals to advertise their social status while others went hungry with little or nothing to eat. The braggarts despised, or thought lightly of, the church of God and shamed those who didn't have much (1 Cor. 11:22).

4. Read 1 Corinthians 11:27–34. Summarize Paul's message to the Corinthians on the matter of misusing the Lord's Supper.

Still others see church as a competition for the title of holiest member. These people will make sure they are seen "serving" in the church. They will talk about their "humble" service for God and how many hours they have invested in it. The Corinthians who claimed to be disciples of Paul, Apollos, Cephas, or Christ reflected this desire to be seen as the holiest (1 Cor. 1:10–12). Paul reminded them that Christ was not divided (1:13). And Christ had not chosen them because they were "wise," "mighty," and "noble" (1:26). This meant they had no reason to glory in themselves (1:29). If anyone was to glory, it was to be in the Lord (1:31).

5. Why might some believers treat church as a club, runway, or competition?

Church is not a club, a runway, or a competition. It is God's program and therefore a heavenly institution. When we understand the church's heavenly origin, we should treat it seriously rather than flippantly and selfishly.

The Church Is a Product of God's Wisdom

The apostle Paul talked about God's grand plan in Romans 11. He explained how God has set aside Israel to deal with the rest of humanity (Gentiles). God is not done with Israel. One day they will return to Him, and He will again deal directly with His people (11:25–27). But until then, the church is God's main focus.

As Paul contemplated God's plan, he couldn't help but praise God for His "wisdom and knowledge" (11:33). Both God's wisdom in planning salvation and His knowledge of us are "past finding out." That means we could never fully understand God's mind. It is from this wisdom and knowledge that God planned the church.

6. Read Romans 11:33. What illustration could you use to show the depth of God's wisdom and knowledge?

7. Read Romans 11:34. What is Paul communicating with the two rhetorical questions in this verse?

8. How should believers respond to the fact that God planned the church with His wisdom and knowledge? Add to the list.

- They should take church seriously.
- They should seek to know what God says about the church in His Word.
- They should not try to make it something God never intended it to be.

Because the local church is God's program for this age, nothing should be more important to us. We should be in tune with what God wants to accomplish in the church. Church should not be something we do on the side; we should devote our lives to serving Christ in the context of the church.

We should also want to know what our part is in God's program. Instead of worrying about whether a church fits our style or meets our needs, we ought to be rolling up our sleeves and asking to be part of the work.

Christ Is the Church's Foundation and Founder

While church is part of God's wise plan, it is Christ Who is its founder, foundation, builder, and instructor. Learning Christ's roles will help us better understand the importance of the church. As a result, we should never think of church as ho-hum. Christ's investment in it was too high to ever make church unimportant.

Most organizations have a founder; none of those founders would also call themselves the foundation of the organization. Christ is both the founder and foundation of the church.

Picking up the topic of schisms in the church at Corinth, Paul wrote about Christ's role as the foundation of the church. Paul said he laid the foundation and that others built on it. Paul laid the foundation by preaching the gospel. He then made it clear that Christ is the only foundation for the church that anyone could lay (1 Cor. 3:11).

9. Read 1 Corinthians 3:11. Why can the church have no other foundation than Christ?

Christ made the ultimate investment in the church by laying down His life for it. By rising from the dead, He became the foundation of the church. Without Christ's death and resurrection, the church is meaningless and our faith is worthless (1 Cor. 15:17).

Christ is also the church's founder in the sense that He started the church. He first talked of the church's beginning to His disciples as part of a conversation about His identity. Peter spoke up and rightly said that Jesus is the "Christ, the Son of the living God" (Matt. 16:16, 17).

Christ then said He would build His church on "this rock" (16:18). The context does not say who or what the "rock" is. Most likely it is Christ when passages like 1 Corinthians 3:11 are taken into consideration. So Christ became the foundation for the church and then started building the church as its founder.

Christ Is the Church's Builder and Head

Some people think that since Jesus said He would build His church then all they need to do is get out of the way and let Him do His building. Consequently, they don't reach out to the lost to evangelize them, and they don't even make much of an effort to get to know their neighbors. They figure that Jesus will do the work for them. What they don't understand is that Jesus does the work *through* them, not *for* them. Jesus is building His church, but He does it through believers.

As the church's builder, Jesus is also the head of the church (Eph. 1:22, 23; Col. 1:18). All believers make up His body. Each local church, then, is a microcosm of the entire group of believers that make up the total body of Christ (1 Cor. 12:12, 13).

This head and body metaphor helps us understand both Christ's role and the church's role in building the church. Christ empowers the church, His body, through the Spirit. And the Spirit gives believers spiritual gifts to use in service (12:11). Christ also feeds His body by His Word and loves His body (Eph. 5:25–30). Believers then serve as Christ directs them. They are His hands and feet in ministry. As they reach out in His power and under His direction, Christ works through them. Souls are saved and discipled. Christ's church is built! And the glory goes to Christ.

10. How does understanding that Christ is the head and builder of your church motivate you to be a part of the work of the church?

Christ Is the Church's Instructor

As its head, Christ commissioned the church to make disciples (Matt. 28:18–20). Part of the disciple-making process involves teaching what Christ commanded. This is not simply a reference to whatever Christ commanded while He was on earth. It mainly refers to the commands Jesus gave through those who wrote the Epistles.

11. Read John 16:12–15. Whose words did the Holy Spirit declare to the writers of the Epistles?

Christ provided the Epistles as the instruction manual for making disciples. The rest of the Bible is valuable to us (2 Tim. 3:16, 17) in that it teaches us about God, His plan, His interaction with people, and how people of faith related to God. But the bulk of the directives for the church are found in the Epistles.

While the Bible makes it clear that we are not under the law, we are under grace (Rom. 6:16–22). That does not mean we are free from any commands and that we have a free pass to sin as we please. Grace gives us guidelines for life as a believer. As a result, there are numerous commands for believers in the Epistles.

In commissioning the church, Christ gave the command to make disciples, the only imperative found in His instructions. So when the church teaches what Christ commanded, His command to make disciples should be part of what they teach. Disciple makers, then, teach disciples to become disciple makers.

12. What would happen to your church if every member followed the Great Commission and made disciple-making disciples?

The Pastor Equips the Church to Serve

Though Christ has an active, leading role in the church, He appoints pastors to work under Him. That does not mean the rest of the church becomes spectators as the pastor works. Nor does it mean the pastor grabs all the work and doesn't let anyone else get involved.

13. Read Ephesians 4:11, 12. What is the pastor's main role in the church?

Inactive churches might conclude that they have contributed their part to the work of the ministry by simply paying their pastor. If his workload is too much, then they hire an assistant for him. The people in the congregation, after all, have their own jobs and responsibilities to take care of. Of course, on special anniversaries and at Christmas the church pools their resources to recognize the pastor for his hard work. They pat him on the back and give him a gift or check and hope he doesn't expect them to get too involved in actually working in the church.

14. How should a mostly inactive church show their overloaded pastor their appreciation?

Sitting idly by and praying your pastor will have strength to do *all* the work of the ministry is a prayer God simply won't hear.

15. How should an inactive church pray for their pastor?

The Church Is to Honor Its Pastor

Some church members need to be less active. Namely, those members who try to control and mold their pastor into what they think he should be. Needling comments, critical notes, and gossip are some of the common ways members attempt to influence their pastor. Others go so far as to make the pastor's life so miserable that he leaves the church.

The pastor shouldn't be above constructive criticism, but he is God's man for the church. And as God's man, the church needs to honor him and support him (1 Cor. 9:9–11, 14).

16. Read Hebrews 13:17. What does God require of church members?

The pastor is responsible to Christ and must give an account to Him for what he did as a steward of Christ's church. His accounting will be with joy if his church was submissive. If not, he will grieve for them, but the church will be the one that will suffer loss, not the pastor (Heb. 13:17).

Some churches take their pastor's ministry flippantly. They move pastors as if they are changing carpet or drapes. It is imperative a church cherish and honor its pastor and treat him as God's man to teach and equip them.

The reality of the connection between how church members respond to their pastor and how they will fair at the Judgment Seat of Christ needs to be rehearsed by each church member. They need to be touched with the thought of their pastor grieving at their lack of response to his spiritual leadership. Positively, those church members who respond to their pastor will cause him much joy as he stands before Christ.

MAKING IT PERSONAL

17. How have you viewed church? Have you seen it as a club, a runway, or a competition?

18. How has your perception of church changed as a result of this lesson?

19. What could you do to be a part of our church's mission of making disciples?

20. How have you responded to your pastor's ministry?

21. What will you do to encourage your pastor? Pray for him? Offer yourself to be active in the work of the church?

God Sends

▶ Scripture Focus

Acts 1:8; 2:1–4; Rom. 12:7, 8; 1 Cor. 12:27, 28; Eph.
2:8–10; 4:11–16; 1 Pet. 4:10, 11

Theme

God commands believers to lovingly exercise their spiritual gifts for
the benefit of the church.

Memory Verse

*"As every man hath received the gift, even so minister the same
one to another, as good stewards of the manifold grace of God"*
(1 Peter 4:10).

GETTING STARTED

Buying gifts for people is not easy. But it is usually best to stay away
from gifts that require the person to work in order to use them. An iron
and jumper cables, for example, don't make good gifts. A new watch or
a pair of diamond earrings are usually better received.

1. How would you react to getting jumper cables as a gift?

2. Why would you feel that way?

Spiritual gifts are mainly for helping other people. But that does
not mean we should regret getting them. Having the opportunity to use
our spiritual gifts to serve others is a tremendous blessing. This study is
about God's reasons for our service and the Spirit's role in our service.

The previous lesson presented the reality of the church. God designed the church as the program for this age. Christ is busy building His Church, and He has chosen to do so through believers in local churches. God expects us to lovingly serve each other as part of a local church.

Serving Fulfills Our Purpose

3. Read Ephesians 2:8, 9. What wrong conclusions might someone draw about works based on this passage?

Emphasizing the grace of God for salvation is of the utmost importance. But God's grace for salvation is not an end in itself. Salvation by grace opens the door for a life of service to God.

"Workmanship" in Ephesians 2:10 refers to the work God is doing in our lives to change us. Lesson six presented the fruit the Holy Spirit produces in our lives as we devote ourselves to God (Rom. 12:1, 2) and as we live dependent on the Spirit (Gal. 5:16). "Workmanship" is a reference to that fruit. We are "in Christ" (Eph. 2:10) at salvation. That allows God to make us like Christ after salvation.

4. According to Ephesians 2:10, why does God want us to be like Christ?

Many believers see good works as optional. What matters most to them is that they are saved and guaranteed eternity in Heaven. But they have missed the fact that good works are the point of their salvation!

5. When did God make His plan for us to do good works (Eph. 2:10)?

There is a lot of talk today about finding yourself and discovering your purpose in life. For a believer, that should never be an issue. We know that God wants us to serve Him, and we can be confident He will let us know where and how He wants us to serve Him.

"That we should walk in them" refers to our lives. Doing good works for the Lord is the point of our lives.

6.   How do you respond to the connection between God's plan for your life and good works?

Serving Glorifies God

As we use our lives to do good works for the Lord, there is always the temptation to make the work all about us. We want people to notice what we are doing. We like the attention. It feeds our egos. But God did not ordain us to do good works so we could have our egos stroked.

7.   Read 1 Peter 4:10, 11. Why does it make sense for God to get the glory for our service for Him?

We can't take the credit for our good works because it is God Who supplies the ability to even do good works. The verb describing the sup- plying of "ability" (4:11) is a strengthened verb for giving and conveys the idea of abundantly supplying.

The fact that God abundantly supplies for our service for Him means that He has given us a stewardship (4:10). He wants us to do something with the supply that He owns and has entrusted to us. He expects us to be faithful in our stewardship (1 Cor. 4:2) and thereby bring Him glory.

8.   What are some ramifications of your service being a stewardship from God? Add to the list.

   • God is counting on me and is expecting me to be a good steward.
   • I must give an account of my stewardship to God.

As we fulfill our purpose to do good works, we bring glory to God because He is the One Who abundantly supplies the ability to serve Him.

Christ's death on the cross makes serving God possible. Peter recognized that and praised Christ, ascribing glory to Him forever and ever (1 Pet. 4:11).

The Spirit Empowers Us to Serve

There could be no true service for God without the Holy Spirit. He supplies the power we need to serve in the church. In the time between Christ's resurrection and ascension, Christ told the disciples to go to Jerusalem and wait for the Holy Spirit. They would receive power once the Holy Spirit came upon them (Acts 1:8). On the Day of Pentecost that is exactly what happened. The Spirit made His presence known with a rushing wind and flames (2:1–4). Immediately the disciples experienced the Spirit's power in their lives.

The church began on the Day of Pentecost. Since that day, the Holy Spirit immediately indwells every person who trusts in Christ as his Savior. Every believer has the same Holy Spirit in him, so all believers are equally empowered to serve the Lord.

9. Since the Spirit is in you, could you ever have a valid excuse for not serving God?

As the Spirit empowers us to serve He also gives us spiritual gifts to use in our service. A spiritual gift is simply an ability God gives us to use in our service for Him. Spiritual gifts are not talents, but we could use our talents as a conduit for our spiritual gifts. For example, a person talented in music could use singing as a way to exercise her gift of exhortation.

10. How much thought have you given to what spiritual gifts you have?

Romans 12, 1 Corinthians 12, Ephesians 4, and 1 Peter 4 all give partial lists of spiritual gifts. From those passages we can compile a master list that helps us consider what spiritual gifts we might have. We can organize these gifts into speaking gifts and serving gifts. First Peter 4:11 uses these two categories to classify spiritual gifts.

The Spirit Gives Speaking Gifts

Speaking gifts include teaching, exhortation, pastor-teacher, and evangelism. **Teaching** (Rom. 12:7) is simply communicating truth from God's Word in an understandable and applicable way. This doesn't preclude a person with the gift of teaching from needing to study God's Word. A good teacher will be diligent to study God's Word thoroughly before teaching it. A good teacher will also seek to hone his teaching skills and get better at using his gift.

The gift of **exhortation** (Rom. 12:8) is the ability to encourage someone going through a difficult circumstance. The encouragement is not just making a person feel better; it is spiritual in nature and helps the person respond to the circumstance in a godly way. This gift might also be used to motivate people to participate in the ministry of the church.

Pastor-teacher (Eph. 4:11) is both a spiritual gift and a position in the church. All men called by God to be a pastor will have the gift of pastor-teacher. Pastoring is a reference to caring for people. Teaching is mentioned above. Those who aspire to be pastors need to meet the qualifications laid out in 1 Timothy 3:1–7.

Evangelism (Eph. 4:11) is the gift of being able to communicate the gospel clearly and effectively. God expects every believer to evangelize. Those with the gift of evangelism should train other believers to evangelize effectively.

11. Who do you think has a speaking gift? Write their names next to the appropriate gift.

    - Teaching
    - Exhortation
    - Pastor-teacher
    - Evangelism

12. How have individuals with speaking gifts helped you?

The Spirit Gives Serving Gifts

Ministering (Rom. 12:7) is the gift of meeting needs. Deacons should have this gift since they are responsible for meeting members' needs

(Acts 6:1–7). Those with this gift are particularly good at understanding needs and finding ways to meet them.

The gift of **giving** (Rom. 12:8) refers to those who give of themselves to the Lord. They might give their money, time, or abilities. What is given is not as important as the attitude with which it is given. Consequently a person with this gift does not have to be rich.

Ruling (Rom. 12:8) is the gift of being able to help a church understand and fulfill its purpose. Those with this gift work with the church's pastor with an attitude of humility and service. They will help him with vision for the ministry and with communicating that vision.

God gives some people the gift of **mercy** (Rom. 12:8). They can comfort and strengthen the hurting as they exercise their gift. They empathize with the hurting and minister to their hearts.

Helps (1 Cor. 12:28) is the gift of assisting in ministry. Often those with this gift are working behind the scenes to do what others will overlook.

Those with the gift of **administration** (1 Cor. 12:28) work with both the pastor and those with the gift of ruling. They organize and run ministries in the church that help to fulfill its mission. They also enlist and train people to work in the ministries.

13. Who do you think has a serving gift? Write their names next to the appropriate gift.

    - Ministering
    - Giving
    - Ruling
    - Mercy
    - Helps
    - Administration

14. Give an example of how a person with one of these gifts has helped you.

We should never let ignorance of our exact spiritual gifts keep us from serving. We should be more concerned about being willing to serve God (1 Pet. 4:10). But there are three questions that help us understand what our spiritual gifts are.

First, what do you like to do? Using your spiritual gifts is enjoyable when you are devoted to God and dependent on the Holy Spirit. What you like to do is usually in line with what your gifts are.

Second, what types of service do people say you do well? As you begin to serve God in ways you find enjoyable, other believers will notice your service and recognize what you do well. Their affirmation of your service is a good indicator that you are exercising your spiritual gifts.

Third, what opportunities is God bringing your way? You should not have to search and search for ways to use your spiritual gifts. God in His sovereignty will give you opportunities to use your gifts.

15. Based on these three questions, what spiritual gifts do you think you might have?

Our Service Edifies

God intends for us to use our spiritual gifts for the benefit of other believers. Other believers are counting on us to do our part in ministry.

The word "minister" in 1 Peter 4:10 means to be a servant. The idea is to wait on each other as each other's servants. At first read, that might seem like a raw deal. But Paul gives more insight into the benefits of using our spiritual gifts.

Using our spiritual gifts causes a "manifestation" (1 Cor. 12:7) of the Spirit. We make the Spirit known when we use the spiritual gifts we received from Him. The exercise of our gifts reveals His presence, His power, and His character. The Holy Spirit is magnified by the use of spiritual gifts.

16. According to 1 Corinthians 12:7, who profits when believers serve each other through exercising their gifts?

The whole church profits from our exercising of our spiritual gifts because all members are connected in the body of Christ. When we serve a member of Christ's body, we are also helping ourselves. If your hand were to refuse to clean and bandage a wound on your knee, the hand would only be hurting itself because it is part of the same body as the knee. An infection in the knee would affect the hand and the rest of the body.

God designed the local church to function as a body and to build itself up through the exercise of spiritual gifts (Eph. 4:11, 12). The pastor equips the people to minister. Part of that equipping ministry includes using the Word to spiritually prepare members to serve. Remember, believers are God's "workmanship" (Eph. 2:10), a reference to the spiritual work God is doing in their lives to change them to be like Christ. There is a measure of spiritual growth that needs to happen in a believer before he is equipped to use his spiritual gifts to their fullest, though even brand new believers can serve God in some capacity right away. Once the believer matures and begins to use his gifts, he helps others grow spiritually. The pastor's ministry in essence multiplies every time a believer begins to exercise his gifts in the church.

As more believers respond to the pastor's equipping, the church begins to function as a body. When the body works together, its individual parts become stronger. In other words, the body begins "edifying" itself.

17. Read Ephesians 4:13–16. What happens when the church edifies itself through the mutual exercise of spiritual gifts?

"Love" (Eph. 4:16) is vital to edification within a church. If members do not have love for one another, then they won't build each other up in the faith. The absence of love in a church is actually evidence of a lack of Spirit-led believers because love is a fruit of the Spirit (Gal. 5:22). We show love as we learn to depend on the Spirit and live according to His enabling.

A pastor's job is never done, especially if new believers are being added to the church regularly. But even longtime members need to be fed from the Word so they might continue to mature. No church will ever become absolutely perfect. But that is still the goal. A church and its pastor should not lose sight of the goal to measure up to Christ.

MAKING IT PERSONAL

18. Do you know your spiritual gifts? If not, review the questions to ask yourself to get you started.

19. If everyone in your church used their spiritual gifts as much as you do, what condition would your church be in?

20. What could you do to enhance your use of your spiritual gifts? Add to the list.
    • Identify mentors who could help me develop my gifts.
    • Take advantage of any training resources my church offers.

21. What opportunities to use your spiritual gifts will you take advantage of?

Christ Will Reward

▶ Scripture Focus

Various passages

Theme

Christ will reward believers for their service at the
Judgment Seat of Christ.

> ### Memory Verses
> "The four and twenty elders fall down before him that sat on the
> throne, and worship him that liveth for ever and ever, and cast their
> crowns before the throne, saying, Thou art worthy, O Lord, to receive
> glory and honour and power: for thou hast created all things, and
> for thy pleasure they are and were created" (Revelation 4:10, 11).

GETTING STARTED

"And the award goes to . . ." Such a phrase creates a moment of
sometimes intense anticipation. Award candidates spend months and
even years preparing for the award ceremony. Their sacrifice and perse-
verance makes the candidates desirous to hear their names.

1. Why is the past more important than the future at award cere-
    monies?

2. When have you attended an award ceremony with satisfaction
    for your past effort?

3. When have you attended an award ceremony with regret for not
    having done more?

This study is about the future award ceremony called the Judgment Seat of Christ. At that ceremony Christ will reward believers for what they did during their lives on earth. We should anticipate that ceremony by serving Christ now.

SEARCHING THE SCRIPTURES

The previous lesson helped us see that God equips us to serve Him in the context of a local church. This lesson will help us make the connection between our service on earth and our rewards at the Judgment Seat of Christ.

Timing of the Judgment Seat of Christ

The next event in God's dealing with humanity is the Rapture. The Rapture is Christ's return for His bride, the church. All believers from the coming of the Holy Spirit on the Day of Pentecost until the Rapture are part of the church. When Christ returns, He will not come all the way to earth. He will first resurrect believers who have died and then He'll rapture the living believers to meet Him in the air (1 Thess. 4:15–17). All believers will immediately have a glorified body and will return to Heaven with Christ (1 Cor. 15:50–53).

Christ will then judge each believer at the Judgment Seat of Christ (2 Cor. 5:10). He will give believers crowns based on what they did while on earth, rewarding all service that He deems good. The word "bad" is a reference to the service we do for God that is not worthy of a crown.

The Rapture will mark the end of the opportunity for living believers to earn rewards at the Judgment Seat of Christ. The Rapture will happen instantaneously (1 Cor. 15:52). The word "moment" means "an indivisible amount of time." "In the twinkling of an eye" refers to the eye's very rapid movement. It is another indication of the swiftness of the Rapture. In addition, Jesus said in Revelation 22:12 that He is coming "quickly," yet another reference to the speed at which the Rapture will happen.

4. Why would Jesus want us to know that the Rapture will happen instantaneously and without warning?

Christ's coming should affect our lives as we look forward to it. Paul wrote to Titus about anticipating Christ's return.

5. Read Titus 2:11, 12. How should the coming of Christ affect our lives?

6. Read Titus 2:13. "Looking for" means to "receive favorably." Why might a believer not receive the return of Christ favorably?

Believers should look forward to Christ's return as a "blessed hope" or happy anticipation (Titus 2:13).

7. What particular events in your life have you happily anticipated? How did your anticipation affect your life?

We should anticipate Christ's return more than any other event in our lives. In our anticipation, we should be actively serving God. But we must be careful how we serve. Christ will not reward all good works with crowns.

Qualifications for the Crowns

Peter gives instructions about what service will qualify for a crown (1 Pet. 4:10, 11). Believers are to serve God with God's abundant supply of strength rather than with their own strength. And their motivation should be to glorify God instead of themselves. Those who follow these guidelines will earn crowns through their service.

8. What might be some clues that a believer serves God in his own strength?

Desiring the glory for our service usually indicates that we are serving in our own strength. Peter's instructions make that clear. He says to minister with God's "ability" that "God in all things may be glorified" (4:11). "That" introduces a purpose clause and links serving in God's strength with glorifying God through the service.

9. What might be some clues that a believer wants the glory for his service?

Those who serve God in His strength will recognize that God deserves all the glory for their service. Yet Christ will give *them* the crowns.

10. Read 1 Corinthians 3:10–12. What would a fire do to a building made of wood, hay, and stubble?

Those who serve God in their own strength and for their own glory are metaphorically building on the foundation of Christ with very combustible materials. That is bad news. That material won't stand up to Christ's scrutiny at the Judgment Seat.

11. Read 1 Corinthians 3:13–15. How much attention should you pay to your "building materials"?

Salvation is not the issue at the Judgment Seat of Christ; the quality of building materials is the issue. We must serve God in His strength and for His glory. Otherwise we will forfeit any crowns we would have received. We will enter Heaven smelling like smoke without much to show for our life on earth.

Descriptions of the Crowns

Several passages give us descriptions of specific crowns a believer could receive at the Judgment Seat. The list is not exhaustive, but it does give us a glimpse of what Christ will reward when He judges us.

The first reward is the **incorruptible crown** (1 Cor. 9:25). Those who show personal discipline as they are serving Christ will receive this crown. That means keeping our bodies under control and ordering our lives to include time for spiritual disciplines like prayer and Bible study.

12. Read 1 Corinthians 9:24, 25. How does comparing the believer to a world-class runner help you understand the discipline it takes to receive this crown?

Paul sought the incorruptible crown. He disciplined his body and brought it under subjection lest he become disqualified for the prize (1 Cor. 9:26, 27).

Christ will award the **crown of rejoicing** to those who have won souls to the Lord and have seen them grow in Christ (1 Thess. 2:19, 20). Paul said the Thessalonians would in essence be his crown of rejoicing at the return of Christ.

Near the end of Paul's life he recounted his faithfulness for God. He had "fought a good fight," "finished" his "course," and "kept the faith" (2 Tim. 4:7, 8). Therefore the **crown of righteousness** awaited him at the Judgment Seat. Faithfulness is the key to receiving the crown of righteousness. Paul was faithful with all that God entrusted to him.

13. Read 2 Timothy 4:7, 8. What is the connection between loving Christ's appearing and faithfulness to God throughout life?

Believers who endure temptation will receive the **crown of life** (James 1:12). When trials come, it is tempting to give up on God and quit. Christ will reward those who persevere.

14. Read James 1:12. What will motivate those who endure temptation?

Love is the key to enduring temptation. Trials tempt us to doubt God's goodness. We wonder if He really cares for us. Our love for Him in response to His love for us helps us endure.

The final crown is for pastors. Pastors who are willing to serve, eager to serve, and exemplary in their service will receive the crown of glory (1 Pet. 5:1–4). This crown has nothing to do with which pastor had the largest building or the greatest attendance. The pastor's heart is the focus of this crown that "fadeth not away."

We Will Worship around God's Throne

What will we do with the crowns Christ gives us at the Judgment Seat of Christ? We will use them to worship Him.

John recorded a heavenly scene that reveals the valuableness of our crowns (Rev. 4). God brought John into Heaven in spirit to give him a revelation of things to come. The revelation started in the throne room of God. The sight of God's throne captured John's attention immediately. John described God's appearance like a "jasper" and a "sardine" (sardius) stone (4:3). Jasper stones are translucent and come in various colors, red in particular. Sardius stones are also translucent and either yellowish brown or red. God must have been veiling His glory in some way, for John could not have looked on God's full glory and lived. Around God's throne was a rainbow that was like an emerald in appearance (4:3). The twenty-four elders seated around the throne most likely represent the church, the Body of Christ (4:4).

Also around the throne were four living creatures. They worshiped the Lord God Almighty for His holiness (4:6–8). The fact that they repeat the word "holy" three times is a testimony to the completeness of God's holiness. The fact that they worship God day and night shows that no amount of praise could ever be enough to recognize the awesomeness of God.

15. Read Revelation 4:9–11. Why do the twenty-four elders cast their crowns before the throne?

God empowers us to serve Him, so He deserves all the glory for what He accomplishes through us. Furthermore our crowns will be a result of God's grace. We don't deserve Heaven, and we certainly don't deserve to receive crowns when we get there. The Lord will give us crowns anyway because He is gracious. We will realize that fact and will use our crowns to worship God around His throne as a result.

We Will Worship God for All Eternity

The book of Revelation describes multiple scenes of worship of God. All of them are still future. The Tribulation believers worship God after being delivered from the troubles and persecution of the Tribulation (Rev. 7:9–17). They are so grateful for their salvation that they feel compelled to serve God day and night (7:15). Worship is obviously a part of their service.

The church worships the Lord God Almighty at the announcement of the transfer of the kingdoms of the world to Christ (11:15–19). The church gives thanks to the Lord God Almighty for asserting His power to reign over the earth. The wrath of God is a major focus of this worship. The transfer of power actually happens at the battle of Armageddon (16:13–16; 19:17–21) when Christ returns with the church to defeat the world's armies.

The 144,000 Jews who share the gospel on the earth during the Tribulation sing a new song before God's throne (14:1–5). This scene is most likely in Heaven. Their song is "new" because no one else experienced what they did as part of the Tribulation. They will be able to appreciate and praise God in a way that only they will fully understand.

The next instance of worship in Heaven involves the tribulation martyrs. Though the Antichrist has physically killed them, they are ultimately victorious over him (12:11). They stand on a sea of glass before God's throne. They sing praises to God while playing harps (15:2–4). Their song reflects the song Moses sang to Israel after God destroyed the Egyptians in the Red Sea (Ex. 15:1–21). It also seems to reflect Moses' last song he sang to Israel before his death and Israel's entrance into the Promised Land (Deut. 32:1–43). The truths about God in Moses' songs will be true forever. They will be part of our theme in glory when we all get to Heaven.

In Revelation 19:1–8 the inhabitants of Heaven worship God for the victory over Babylon. The sound of the praise is like the sound of rushing water and mighty thundering (19:6). The coming reign of the Lord God Omnipotent and the marriage of the Lamb to the church is the focus of their praise (19:6, 7).

16. Read Revelation 19:6. What does the volume of our praise to God tell you about our enthusiasm for worshiping God in Heaven?

17. Do you think that enthusiasm will ever wane throughout eternity? Explain.

The themes for our worship of God in eternity are numerous; we could never wear them out.

The eternal ability to worship God and magnify Him is the reason why we should be certain we are using gold, silver, and precious stones as the building materials in our lives (1 Cor. 3:12–14). Bragging on God is what we will want to do more than anything else in Heaven. Our crowns will be a primary vehicle for magnifying and worshiping God.

Those who created an illusion of living the Christian life will suffer eternal loss of reward at the Judgment Seat of Christ. All believers will enjoy eternity, but those who receive crowns at the Judgment Seat will have an increased capacity to worship God.

MAKING IT PERSONAL

18. What are your thoughts as you consider standing before Christ to receive crowns for what you have done on earth?

19. Evaluate your Christian service. Have you depended on your own power or the Spirit's power to serve the Lord? Explain.

20. Have you served for your own glory and recognition or for the glory and recognition of the Lord? Explain.

Be active in serving the Lord in the power of the Spirit and for the glory of the Lord. Such service demands a conscious effort, but the reward for it will be eternally fulfilling and enjoyable!

21. What might you need to change in your service to God to ensure you are building with "gold, silver, and precious stones"?

Christ Will Judge

▶ Scripture Focus

Various passages

Theme

God will judge unbelievers for their sins, condemning them to eternity in the Lake of Fire.

> ### Memory Verses
>
> *"And I saw the dead, small and great, stand before God; and the books were opened: and another book was opened, which is the book of life: and the dead were judged out of those things which were written in the books, according to their works. And whosoever was not found written in the book of life was cast into the lake of fire"* (Revelation 20:12, 15).

GETTING STARTED

"Danger! High Voltage!" is a warning of *imminent* danger. If you ignore that sign, you will most likely be severely injured or even killed. "Bridge May Be Icy" is a warning of *possible* danger. That sign seems absolutely ridiculous when the temperature is soaring in the middle of July.

1. What kind of "warning sign" should believers raise when talking to the lost about eternity?

2. Why might believers fail to raise an imminent danger warning sign when talking to the lost?

The Bible has a lot to say about God's coming judgment on the lost. If we ignore that reality the lost certainly will too. We must be careful to be honest with the lost and to raise the warning of imminent danger. This study will challenge you to share the gospel in light of God's coming judgment on the lost.

The previous lesson presented the opportunity the church has to serve God now so they might receive crowns at the Judgment Seat of Christ. This lesson will focus on the terrible events happening on earth while the church is in Heaven receiving their rewards. It will also cover the condemnation of all the lost of all the ages at the Great White Throne Judgment.

Timing of the Tribulation Judgments

While the church is in Heaven receiving their crowns (2 Cor. 5:10) and participating in the marriage to Christ (Rev. 19:7–10), the inhabitants on earth experience the unleashing of God's wrath on their sin.

God will judge unbelieving humanity to draw Israel back to Himself (Jer. 30) and to pour out His wrath on the world (Rev. 3:10; Isa. 26:21). There is nothing that happens during the Tribulation that unbelieving humanity won't deserve. It is only by God's grace that He allows anyone now to have enjoyment in life outside of a relationship with Him. No one would survive God's wrath if we all received what we deserved.

The pouring out of God's wrath on earth will happen during the Tribulation. The Tribulation will begin sometime after the Rapture when the Antichrist signs a peace treaty with Israel (Dan. 9:27), and it will end seven years later with the second advent of Christ (Rev. 19:11–16).

Descriptions of the Tribulation Judgments

The book of Revelation describes God's judgment on the lost during the Tribulation. This study does not cover each of those judgments in detail, but even a survey of the judgments will help you realize how terrible life will be for those on earth during the Tribulation.

John continued his account of the events happening in God's throne room. He reported that Jesus, the Lamb of God, took a scroll from the Father. The scroll is the title deed to the earth. Only Jesus has the right to open the seven seals on the title deed because He died to pay the penalty for sin. As He opens each seal, events unfold that bring about God's judgment on the earth. The seventh seal brings seven trumpets. As an angel sounds each trumpet, more events occur. The seventh trumpet brings about seven bowls that are figuratively poured out on the earth. They bring the events leading to the end of the Tribulation.

The **seal judgments** include the coming of the Antichrist; worldwide war; severe famine; widespread death by war, hunger, and wild animals; martyrdom of believers; and cosmic disturbances (Rev. 6).

3. Read Revelation 6:12–14. Describe the destruction and chaos that the world will face when the sixth seal is opened.

4. Read Revelation 6:15–17. What will the inhabitants of the earth, including the rich and kings, realize about the source of the cataclysmic disasters?

The world will call on the mountains to fall on them. They will want to escape God's wrath and be out of His sight. They will want the circumstances to end, and they will want to avoid answering to God. But they will hide and cry out in vain.

5. How does reading about the seal judgments affect your appreciation for salvation?

The **trumpet judgments** will bring about more destruction and despair. The first four trumpets will result in hail and fire striking a third of vegetation, a third of the sea becoming blood, a third of the rivers being made poisonous, and a third of the heavens being darkened (8:7–13).

Trumpets five, six, and seven are called the three woes. They include some kind of insects or creatures tormenting the lost for five months, the destruction of a third of mankind by a demon-led army, and the transfer of the nations of the world to Christ's rule (9; 11:15–19).

The **bowl judgments** will occur near the end of the Tribulation. They will include sores on the lost, death of sea creatures as the seas turn to blood, rivers turning to blood, the sun scorching mankind, darkness and pain, the amassing of armies at Armageddon, and a massive earthquake accompanied by gigantic hailstones (16).

6. Read Revelation 16:5–7. What will the angel who pours out the third bowl say about the Lord's judgments?

All of God's judgments on the world throughout the Tribulation will be "true and righteous" (16:7). He will be right in pouring out His wrath. The world will deserve to experience it. That is a scary thought for those who are alive during the Tribulation.

The Tribulation will not be a time for God to show His grace by providing for and caring for the needs of the lost. Rather God will show His grace by overtly judging sin. God's severe judgments will show the world He is a holy God Who must judge sin.

7. What is your reaction to the coming chaos and destruction in the Tribulation?

Responses to the Tribulation Judgments

There will be two clear responses to God's judgment by the end of the Tribulation. Some will harden their hearts and reject God while some will trust in Jesus as their Savior.

8. Read Revelation 16:9, 11, 21. Why will many of the lost not repent in response to the tremendous outpouring of God's wrath?

God will send witnesses out into the world to share the gospel as He is pouring out His judgment on the world. The witnesses will be another measure of God's grace.

During the first half of the Tribulation God will send two unidentified witnesses to Jerusalem (Rev. 11:1–14). They will have special powers from God to perform miracles and control creation. They will be martyred and then rise from the dead in the middle of the Tribulation. God will call them to Heaven as a deadly earthquake strikes Jerusalem. The world's rejoicing over the death of the witnesses is a testimony to the witnesses' effectiveness (11:10).

God will also choose 144,000 Jews to apparently witness throughout the world in the midst of the troubles of the Tribulation (7:4). These Jews will be protected by God during the Tribulation. They will enter the Millennial Kingdom as subjects to Christ's rule.

9.   Read Revelation 7:9–17. What will be the results of the Jews' witness?

The fact that a great multitude of people are saved in the Tribulation is reflective of God's gracious heart. But His gracious desire for men to be saved must be balanced with His wrath against sin. God hates sin, and the sinner who does not repent will not go unpunished.

The Timing of the Final Judgment

The Tribulation will end with the Second Advent of Christ (Rev. 19:11–16). He will return to earth with the church to establish His Kingdom. To prepare for His Kingdom, He will put to death all those who are lost (Isa. 11:4; Rev. 19:15) and will confine Satan to the Bottomless Pit (20:1–3). Believers from the Tribulation who are still living will enter the Millennium. They will be Christ's subjects in His Kingdom (20:4). They will marry and have children who will grow up and also have children. This population growth will continue for the entire thousand-year reign of Christ. Those born in the Millennium will need to put their faith in Christ. They won't automatically be believers.

At the end of Christ's rule, God will give the order for Satan to be released from the Bottomless Pit (20:7). Satan will go throughout the earth to deceive those who have not trusted in Christ (20:8). They will gather together to try to overthrow Christ. God will send fire from Heaven to destroy them and cast Satan into the Lake of Fire, where he will spend eternity (20:9, 10).

God will then resurrect the unbelievers of all the ages to judge them (20:12). The Bible calls Jesus' throne at this judgment a "great white throne" (20:11), so we call it the Great White Throne Judgment.

Christ will judge the lost from the books of works and from the Book of Life (20:12, 13). The Book of Life records the names of those who have trusted in Christ as their Savior. The books of works will give incriminating evidence of sin. Christ will condemn to the Lake of Fire all those who are not found written in the Book of Life (20:15). No one who stands before the Great White Throne Judgment will be found in the Book of Life.

Descriptions of the Final Judgment

The Bible gives details about the torments of the Lake of Fire. Nothing on earth could compare, for the human body would be destroyed before it could experience the smallest fraction of the full force of the Lake of Fire.

10. Read 2 Thessalonians 1:9. Why is being cut off from the presence of the Lord forever such a terrible state to be in?

God's presence will make Heaven what it is. And the absence of God's presence in the Lake of Fire will make it what it is. Being cut off from God's presence is the pinnacle of the punishments of the Lake of Fire. It means eternal doom with absolutely no hope of escape. It means the judgment will be final and will never end.

11. Read Revelation 20:10. What do we learn about the Lake of Fire from this verse?

12. Read Revelation 14:11. What relief will there be for those in the Lake of Fire?

Those who think the Lake of Fire is a party are sadly mistaken. The torment is beyond imagination and it continues forever. Relief and rest will never come to those in the Lake of Fire.

The Lake of Fire will also be a place of utter darkness (Matt. 8:12; 22:13). No one there will see even the faintest sliver of light ever again. This stands in contrast to the eternal state of the redeemed which will shine forever with the light of Christ (Rev. 21:23; 22:5).

Along with the darkness comes "weeping and gnashing of teeth" (Matt. 8:12; 22:13). The "weeping" signifies sorrow and emotional suffering. "Gnashing of teeth" is a result of the painful agony of the Lake of Fire.

13. What three words would you use to describe the final judgment on the lost?

Our Responsibility in Light of God's Judgment

The severity and finality of Christ's final judgment on the lost are somber truths that should motivate us to share the gospel every day.

We must see people as lost and in desperate need of a Savior. Jesus had this outlook as He carried out His ministry on earth (Matt. 9:35, 36). He saw the lost as sheep having no shepherd. Sheep are in constant danger from predators, from wandering off and getting lost, and from falling into holes or off a cliff. Sheep need a shepherd to protect them and guide them. Jesus likened the multitudes of Jews to sheep without a shepherd. He had "compassion" on them (9:36), meaning He was strongly moved emotionally because of their condition. The Jewish religious leaders were causing the Jews to stray. They provided no shepherding help.

14. Read Matthew 9:37, 38. Why is a field ripe unto harvest a good metaphor for the multitude of lost people?

Jesus proceeded to send twelve apostles into the "harvest field." He gave them special instructions before they embarked to preach the gospel of the kingdom (Matt. 10).

15. Read Matthew 10:27, 28. What was to motivate the apostles as they shared the gospel?

The apostles were anxious and fearful to face the Jews who would oppose the gospel and threaten their lives. But they needed to overcome that fear with awe and respect for God. The Jews could kill the apostles, but they could not destroy their soul. God, on the other hand, has the power to send a sinner to eternal punishment in Hell. The apostles' awe of God was to be their impetus for sharing the gospel.

God's care for the apostles was another motivation for sharing the gospel (Matt. 10:29–31). They could proclaim the gospel because God valued them and knew everything about them, including how many hairs they had on their head. The apostles were obedient to Christ. They shared the gospel throughout Galilee. Later, after Christ's death and resurrection, some of them even gave their lives as they carried out the Great Commission (28:18–20).

Today, God has chosen the church to be His primary means of sharing the gospel. That means witnessing is not an option. God expects us to share the good news of salvation with the world. Knowing the reality of God's judgment on the lost should encourage us to witness every opportunity we get.

MAKING IT PERSONAL

16. Do you see people as lost and in need of salvation from their sins? Does their "lostness" frequently cross your mind?

17. How could you increase your awareness of the imminent danger the lost face every day? Add to the list.
    - Pray for the lost regularly.
    - Review the Biblical reality of eternity without Christ.
    - Don't let the mundane routines of life lull you into thinking life will go on forever as it is.

18. What actions should you take in response to the reality of God's coming judgment on the lost? Add to the list.
    - Ask God for open doors to share the gospel.
    - Get training on how to share the gospel effectively.
    - Be proactive in planning evangelistic opportunities.

Christt Will Rule

▶ Scripture Focus

Matt. 6:19–21; John 14:1–3; Phil. 3:12–21; Col. 3:1–3;
Rev. 21:1—22:6

Theme

Christ will rule for all eternity on the new earth.

Memory Verses

"If ye then be risen with Christ, seek those things which are above, where Christ sitteth on the right hand of God. Set your affection on things above, not on things on the earth" (Colossians 3:1, 2).

GETTING STARTED

Want to understand the futility of finding happiness in things? Take a stroll through a junkyard. There you will find mounds of things people once considered their "thing to end all things." What they were convinced would bring them everlasting happiness is discarded and corroded.

1.   Which of your possessions did you think would be the "thing to end all things"?

2.   What has happened to your desire for the possession since getting it?

This study will help us understand the importance of anticipating eternity with Christ. What we anticipate in life will influence our affections. Our affections need to be set on things above rather than on things on earth.

The previous lesson presented the reality of God's future judgment on the lost in the Tribulation as well as at the Great White Throne Judgment. That is a reality we would like to ignore, but reminding ourselves of it serves to spur us to share the gospel. By contrast, eternity with Christ is a reality we should anticipate every day. As we look forward to Heaven, we should set our affections on things above.

Christ's Presence on the New Earth

After the Great White Throne Judgment, God will destroy the present heavens and earth with fire (2 Pet. 3:10–13). Christ will set up His rule on a new earth and in the New Jerusalem.

Heaven will be a fantastic place to spend eternity. But it won't be the new earth or the amazing New Jerusalem that will capture our attention the most. God's presence with us will be the most wonderful part of Heaven.

3. Read Revelation 21:3. What do you think you will appreciate most about being in God's presence forever?

God dwelt in the Garden of Eden with Adam and Eve until their sin separated them from Him (Rom. 5:12). Later God dwelt in the tabernacle and then the temple. At the appointed time, Jesus came to earth and dwelt with humanity (John 1:14). In the present age, God the Holy Spirit dwells in believers (1 Cor. 6:19, 20). But the continuing presence of our sin nature in our sin-cursed bodies keeps us from fully appreciating God's presence in us. We repeatedly grieve and quench the Holy Spirit by our disobedience (Eph. 4:30; 1 Thess. 5:19). When Christ returns for the church, we will be freed from sin and receive glorified bodies (1 Thess. 4:16, 17). We will enjoy God's presence in Heaven and return with Him to earth to rule in the Millennium. Our presence with God will then continue for eternity on the new earth.

4. What types of memories might trouble us and cause us to cry?

5. Read Revelation 21:4. What will God do to all the memories that cause us to cry?

God will "wipe away all tears" in Heaven. That doesn't mean He will cheer us up when we are feeling blue. It means we will never have a reason to feel sad. We will never have a reason to cry. There will be no more death, no more pain, and no more sorrow. Painful memories will trouble us no more in God's presence in Heaven. No one will cause us harm or hurt our feelings.

Christ said He will make all things new (21:5). Nothing will ever die, decay, or wear out. It is hard to imagine a world without destruction and degeneration. There will be no more wrinkle cream, Tylenol, or Geritol. But we will get used to such a world because it will be that way forever. Christ told John to write because His words are "faithful and true" (21:5; 22:6). He then said to John, "It is done" (21:6). Christ is so powerful and trustworthy that we can peer into eternity and be so confident of Christ's work that it is as if it is already done. Eternity with Christ will happen. It is a future reality we can look forward to with absolute assurance.

Christ will also offer an actual "fountain of water of life freely" to all who thirst (21:6; 22:1) as well as the actual tree of life (22:2). We won't have physical thirst and hunger in Heaven, so this must be referring to the spiritual blessings Christ offers to us. Our souls will be always satisfied and refreshed in Heaven. Christ makes this offer as "the Alpha and Omega, the beginning and the end." Christ is eternal. He always has been and always will be. Christ's offer will stand forever. The satisfying and refreshing blessings of Heaven will never end.

Heaven won't be something we just admire as if we were visiting a museum, though it might seem like that at first. Christ will share the blessings of Heaven with us as heirs (21:7). Heaven will be like owning the museum and living in it. We will have different responsibilities and privileges based on the rewards we receive at the Judgment Seat of Christ, but all of us will be full heirs with Christ (Rom. 8:16, 17). This setting sits in stark contrast to the existence of those who experience eternal death without Christ in the Lake of Fire (Rev. 21:8).

6.   Read Revelation 21:22. Why is it significant that Jesus is called the "Lamb" in this verse?

The fact that the Lord God Almighty and the Lamb are the city's temple means there will be no barriers to God, no veils or walls to separate us from Him. Jesus' scars on His hands, feet, and side will be a reminder of the high price of our redemption. We will forever see Him as the Lamb of God Who took away our sins and allowed us free access to God as His fellow heir.

There won't even be darkness on the new earth (22:5). The Lamb will be its light (21:23). This means the sun and moon will be obsolete.

Christ's New City

Though being with Christ forever will be the best aspect of Heaven, we will thoroughly enjoy Christ's new city, the New Jerusalem.

Jesus was most likely talking about the New Jerusalem when He told His disciples He was leaving to prepare a place for them (John 14:1–3). We are included in this promise. The words "for you" are encouraging in this passage (John 14:2). Jesus is preparing a place for us. The heavenly Home will be personal, a gift from Christ to us. Its description is what you would expect to see coming from Heaven.

7.   Read Revelation 21:2. What would you expect a city to look like that was adorned as a bride for her husband?

The New Jerusalem will be the perfect place to live. God will build it out of love and by His wisdom. Nothing, not even today's grandest metropolis, could ever come close to matching the splendor of the New Jerusalem.

8.   Read Revelation 21:9–21. What two descriptions of the New Jerusalem do you find most fascinating?

Christ's new city will be nearly 1400 miles wide, long, and high! Approximately the same square footage as California, Oregon, Washington, Idaho, Montana, Wyoming, Nevada, Utah, Colorado, Arizona, New Mexico, Texas, Louisiana, Oklahoma, Kansas, Nebraska, South Dakota, and North Dakota combined. That size alone is amazing without mentioning the brilliance of the gold and precious stones that adorn the city's foundation and walls. People often talk about Heaven having "pearly" gates, but each gate will actually be a single large pearl. Clearly God will not hold back when it comes to the splendor of the New Jerusalem. And His building materials will be far beyond the quality you could find on earth. The world's largest and most brilliant jewels would be not be brilliant enough for building materials for the New Jerusalem.

9. Why will God adorn the New Jerusalem so lavishly?

10. Why would God reveal so many details about the New Jerusalem in His Word?

Christ's New Earth

The New Jerusalem will descend from above and will settle on the new earth (21:2). We don't know a lot about the new earth other than it will have "no more sea" (21:1). That does not mean it won't have bodies of water. It just won't have three-fourths of the surface covered with water like our present earth does. The fact that we won't need water to live is probably a reason for not having such a large area of the new earth covered with it.

The new earth will undoubtedly be larger than our current earth. The size of the New Jerusalem would warrant a larger earth. The new earth will also be a perfect environment. The weather will always be enjoyable. There will never be a reason to complain about God's creation.

11. What about this current earth are you glad won't be a part of Heaven?

Apparently there will be people groups or nations on the new earth (21:24). The nations and their kings will "bring their glory and honour" into the New Jerusalem. All glory and honor will belong to Christ. No one will be going to those ruling and reigning with Christ to glorify them (21:25, 26).

Access to the city will never be denied to those written in the "Lamb's book of life" (21:27). The gates will always be swung open. Since there will be no more sin, no one who defiles, abominates, or lies would ever have the opportunity to enter the city.

There will be work to do on the earth (22:3). Work is not a part of the curse. God gave Adam work to do in the Garden of Eden before Adam sinned. Work is just harder now because of the Fall (Gen. 3:17–19). Work in eternity will be fulfilling and enjoyable. There won't be any clock watching or skipping out early in Heaven! Everyone will love their job and be glad for the opportunity to serve Christ.

In our finite minds we cannot fully comprehend what the New Jerusalem and new earth will be like. But God has told us enough details to cause us to anticipate eternity and to desire to live for Him now.

Seek the Things That Are Above

Paul told the Church at Colosse to "seek those things which are above, where Christ sitteth on the right hand of God" (Col. 3:1). Christ's position in Heaven was the focus of lesson 5. Christ is seated in Heaven because of His work on the cross and His resurrection. His presence in Heaven makes seeking Heavenly things worth the effort. His position in Heaven also guarantees us a home in Heaven in eternity (3:3).

The verb "seek" should actually be translated "keep on seeking." This is a lifelong endeavor and encompasses all we are. It is much more than just acknowledging that the "things which are above" are important. And it is more than simply giving lip service to them. It requires action and direction.

The "things which are above" include God's will, His desire for the salvation of mankind, and His desire for believers to serve Him and grow to be like Christ. In other words, the "things above" include that which is real and everlasting. The apostle Paul described his life's focus on becoming like Christ.

12. Read Philippians 3:12–14. Describe Paul's personal testimony about seeking "those things which are above."

The "prize" for Paul was to be glorified by Christ when he reached Heaven. Glorification refers to God taking away our sin nature and giving us a new body untouched by sin and unable to sin. It will take place at the Rapture when the living believers are caught up to Heaven and the dead in Christ are resurrected. Becoming like Christ was Paul's focus as he anticipated his glorification. That focus demanded Paul give his all (Phil. 1:21).

Set Your Mind on Things Above

In Colossians 3:2 Paul urged the Colossians to set their "affection on things above." That means to stay mentally focused on things of God. While we are to be responsible stewards of the possessions God has given to us, we must not let them become what we center our lives around.

13. Read Colossians 3:2. How might you know what your mind is centered on? What are some revealing questions you could ask yourself? Add to the list.

   - What do you get excited about?
   - What occupies your thoughts when you have a moment to think?
   - What do you look forward to?
   - How often do you proactively plan ways to serve Christ?

The worldly mind is focused on "earthly things" (Phil. 3:19). Paul considered those with a worldly mind to be "enemies of the cross of Christ." The cross is about humility and love for others as perfectly demonstrated by Christ (2:6–8). The enemies of the cross want nothing to do with a life of humble service.

14. Read Philippians 3:17–19. What is the focus of those who are enemies of the cross of Christ?

Society treats the present as if it is eternal, living as if this life will last forever. They deny death is coming and try to delay the signs that their bodies are breaking down and dying. Cosmetic injections make old skin appear younger, but it is still old skin. As believers, we must not get caught up in living as if our present life is all there is and that it will last forever. Our attitudes and ambitions should reflect a heavenly focus. We should not live as if we are "unpacked" and here on earth to stay.

Paul viewed earth as a "foreign country" and Heaven as his home (Phil. 3:20, 21). He recognized that his citizenship was in Heaven. So he didn't get comfortable on earth. Instead he used his life to "pack" for Heaven.

15. Describe the attitudes of a person who is "packing" for Heaven.

16. What are the ambitions of a person who is "packing" for Heaven?

When we focus on eternity, we don't waste time investing in earthly endeavors and goals. We won't get attached to this world as if it is all there is to live for. We keep our primary focus on our home in Heaven.

Lay Up Treasure in Heaven

Paul's instructions in Colossians and the example of his life in Philippians are really echoes of what Jesus taught in Matthew 6:19–21. Jesus said not to lay up treasures here on earth because everything on earth is temporary. Critters, corrosion, and criminals all destroy earthly treasures. But none of those destructive forces can tamper with the treasures we lay up in Heaven.

Treasure in Heaven is eternal. It includes the crowns Christ will award at the Judgment Seat. It also includes the results of our service for God here on earth. Those we lead to Christ will be in Heaven forever as will those fellow believers we disciple and train. Those treasures will bring joy to us and glory to God forever.

Jesus said that where our treasure is, there our hearts would be too (6:21). Living for eternity takes heart. It is not something we can do by simply going through the motions. That is why Paul said to stay mentally focused on the things of God (Col. 3:2). And it is why his personal testimony is followed by an appeal to the Philippians to be "thus minded" (Phil. 3:15). He wanted them to share in his press toward the goal of Christlikeness (3:14).

17. What evidence of anticipating eternity is there in your life?

Purposefully anticipate Heaven so your heart and mind will be set on God's work rather than on earthly treasures.

18. Refer back to question 13. Ask yourself the revealing questions to help you begin to understand what your mind is centered on.

Course Wrap-up

Revelation 22:15 describes the people who will spend eternity in the Lake of Fire. The last description is particularly relevant to this course. The verse describes the people as those who love and make, or practice, a lie. In other words, those who make up their own reality and live according to it. This course was designed to challenge you to live in the real, applying Biblical realities to your life. The first lesson talked about the need to wake up spiritually because the lost need you to shine the light of the gospel (1 Cor. 15:34). So what you do with the Biblical realities covered in this course is vital. If you ignore them and decide to live in your own reality as do the lost, you are doing both you and them a grave disservice.

Expect living in the real to take a lifetime, but also expect maturation along the way. Refer to the Biblical realities in this course often until they become part of you. And continue to study the Bible. The Epistles in particular will guide you in living in the real. Get to know them well.